NEW EDITION

LADO ENGLISH SERIES

6 WORKBOOK

by **Robert Lado**

Professor of Linguistics
School of Languages and Linguistics
Georgetown University

in collaboration with

Annette Silverio-Borges

Bernadette Sheridan, I.H.M.

Thea C. Bruhn

Linda Fraser Jacobsen

Regents Publishing Company, Inc.

ACKNOWLEDGEMENTS

Unit 1: "At a Concert, or a Dinner, Some People Just Doze Off," by Enid Nemy, copyright © 1980 by The New York Times Company. Reprinted by permission.

Unit 3: "Elise Rolls Merrily Along on a Bike—at 60," copyright © 1980 by the New York News, Inc. Reprinted by permission.

Illustrations by Richard Toglia

10 9 8 7 6 5

Published by
Regents Publishing Company, Inc.
2 Park Avenue
New York, N.Y. 10016

Printed in the United States of America

ISBN 0-88345-339-8

Table of Contents

	Page
Preface	3
Inventory Test 1	5
Reference Key for Inventory Test 1	8
Refresher Unit	9
Inventory Test 2	29
Reference Key for Inventory Test 2	32
Unit 1	33
Unit 2	45
Unit 3	55
Unit 4	65
Unit 5	75
Unit 6	84
Unit 7	95
Unit 8	105
Unit 9	115
Unit 10	124

Preface

The new edition of the *Lado English Series* is a complete course in English consisting of six carefully graded levels. There is a textbook, workbook, teacher's manual, and cassettes for each level. The central objective of the series is to help students understand, speak, read, and write English. In this edition, careful attention has been given to the importance of using these four skills for meaningful communication.

Workbook 6 provides additional practice in listening comprehension, speaking, reading, writing, and composition for students using Book 6 of the series. It can be used for classwork or homework.

The workbook begins with an **Inventory Test** covering the material taught in Level 5. It is a diagnostic test which singles out the points of pronunciation and grammar that the students have not yet mastered. The test items are keyed to the parts of a **Refresher Unit,** which summarizes the material taught in the preceding level. Students need only review the parts which correspond to the test items they have missed. A second Inventory Test follows, also keyed to the Refresher Unit. The second test is a final check to see whether all the material has been learned. This section of the workbook will provide a useful review not only for those students who have completed Book 5, but also for those who have studied different curricula.

The workbook contains exercises of seven different types: Complete, Write, Listen, Vocabulary in Context, Read, Composition, and Word Game. Each section is designed to strengthen the development of the different language skills.

The **Complete** section may be filled in after the students have mastered the conversation of the corresponding unit in Book 6.

The exercises in the **Write** section can be done after the students have completed the corresponding Study frames and Practice sections in the textbook.

In the **Listen** section the students listen to sentences or brief dialogues. Comprehension is tested by multiple-choice items. The sentences and dialogues to be read to the students can be found in the Workbook Answer Key in Teacher's Manual 6. They are also recorded on the cassettes for Book 6, and can be played for the students.

The **Vocabulary in Context** section provides a review of the new vocabulary with attention focused on meaning. The students choose one of the words or phrases listed to complete in writing one of the sentences.

The **Read** section is intended for silent reading. Comprehension is checked by means of multiple-choice exercises.

The **Composition** section provides practice in organized writing. The exercises progress from controlled writing practice to freer composition. They may be done individually in class or as homework.

The **Word Game** can be done by students individually as writing practice or in two groups as a competition. This exercise provides a review of new and old vocabulary. The emphasis is on compound words and semantic categories.

The students can generally correct their own exercises if the teacher gives them the answers orally or writes them on the board. The answers to all the exercises are given at the end of Teacher's Manual 6. Having students exchange workbooks for correction and then return them to the original students for checking is another effective way to get students to review their errors. It is also necessary for the teacher to check the workbooks occasionally in order to motivate students and to monitor their performance.

The workbook exercises reinforce the students' understanding of the material presented in Book 6 and expand the variety of situations in which the students learn to use the language. In all, the combination of textbook, workbook, and cassettes gives them a wide range of experience in learning to communicate in English.

Inventory Test 1

Check the box next to the word which correctly completes the statement or question.

Example: It's necessary _____ a passport when you travel abroad.
- ☐ a. carrying
- ☐ b. carry
- ☐ c. for carry
- ☑ d. to carry

1. Many trees _____ by disease in recent years.
- ☐ a. have attacked
- ☐ b. have been attacking
- ☐ c. are attacked
- ☒ d. have been attacked

2. _____ a bicycle is good exercise.
- ☐ a. Ride
- ☐ b. A ride
- ☒ c. Riding
- ☐ d. For riding

3. The store was having a _____ .
- ☐ a. sale winter hat
- ☒ b. winter hat sale
- ☐ c. hat sale winter
- ☐ d. winter sale hat

4. Driving _____ car is enjoyable.
- ☐ a. Italian nice
- ☐ b. an Italian nice
- ☒ c. a nice Italian
- ☐ d. nice Italian

5. It's difficult _____ to travel alone.
- ☐ a. for a blind person
- ☐ b. by a blind person
- ☒ c. to a blind person
- ☐ d. a blind person

6. She's _____ short to reach the top shelf.
- ☒ a. too
- ☐ b. very
- ☐ c. enough
- ☐ d. such

7. Mathematics isn't easy to learn and languages _____ .
- ☐ a. aren't
- ☐ b. isn't either
- ☐ c. are too
- ☒ d. aren't either

8. The dinner was excellent, and the _____ was fun.
- ☐ a. after dance
- ☒ b. afterwards dance
- ☐ c. dance afterwards
- ☐ d. afterwards

5

9. By 1930, silent films _____ by talking pictures.
- [x] a. should be replaced
- [ ] b. had been replaced
- [ ] c. have been replaced
- [ ] d. are being replaced

10. Many high school students want to go to college, but Frank Brown _____ .
- [ ] a. don't
- [x] b. doesn't
- [ ] c. does too
- [ ] d. doesn't either

11. The robbery victims didn't expect _____ alive.
- [ ] a. escaping
- [ ] b. escape
- [x] c. to escape
- [ ] d. for escaping

12. Sarah seemed anxious _____ home early.
- [ ] a. got
- [x] b. to get
- [ ] c. getting
- [ ] d. get

13. I have to make _____ every morning.
- [ ] a. the cleaning
- [ ] b. the dishes
- [ ] c. my homework
- [x] d. breakfast

14. The hikers watched the sun _____ .
- [ ] a. gone down
- [x] b. went down
- [ ] c. it goes down
- [ ] d. go down

15. The people in _____ the countries of South America speak Spanish.
- [ ] a. the most of
- [x] b. most of
- [ ] c. most
- [ ] d. the most

16. Mexico is in North America and Canada _____ .
- [ ] a. is
- [ ] b. is so
- [ ] c. isn't either
- [x] d. is too

17. If we _____ control pollution, we won't be able to live on earth.
- [x] a. don't
- [ ] b. wouldn't
- [ ] c. didn't
- [ ] d. couldn't

18. It's difficult _____ the piano well.
- [x] a. to play
- [ ] b. to playing
- [ ] c. play
- [ ] d. of playing

19. _____ guests to arrive were Alice and Bob.
- [ ] a. The first two
- [x] b. The two first
- [ ] c. First two
- [ ] d. Two first

20. While Toshi was studying in Rome, he _____ many famous monuments.
- [ ] a. visits
- [x] b. visited
- [ ] c. will visit
- [ ] d. has visited

21. If fewer people _____ to work, there would be less pollution.
- [x] a. drive
- [ ] b. drove
- [ ] c. have driven
- [ ] d. are driving

22. After the last note of the symphony, the audience started _____ loudly.
- [ ] a. for clapping
- [ ] b. clap
- [x] c. clapping
- [ ] d. by clapping

23. Bob isn't tall _____ to play basketball.
- [x] a. enough
- [ ] b. very
- [ ] c. much
- [ ] d. too

24. Taking photographs is easy if you _____ careful.
- [x] a. are
- [ ] b. be
- [ ] c. was
- [ ] d. were

25. The meeting was delayed _____ the bad weather.
- [ ] a. because
- [ ] b. because of
- [ ] c. for
- [x] d. from

26. Photography is a _____ hobby.
- [x] a. fascinating
- [ ] b. fascination
- [ ] c. fascinated
- [ ] d. fascinate

27. A sick person should not postpone _____ the doctor.
- [ ] a. see
- [x] b. to see
- [ ] c. seeing
- [ ] d. from seeing

28. Some libraries save only _____ copies of a book.
- [ ] a. two most recent
- [ ] b. the most recent two
- [x] c. the two most recent
- [ ] d. most recent two

29. Many tons of paper _____ for newspapers everyday.
- [x] a. are used
- [ ] b. used
- [ ] c. are using
- [ ] d. have used

30. Why does Bill go out so much? _____ fun.
- [ ] a. Have
- [x] b. To have
- [ ] c. Has
- [ ] d. Having

7

Reference Key for Inventory Test 1

If you missed any items on Inventory Test 1, locate the number of each item on the list below and study the corresponding section in the Refresher Unit.

Inventory Test Item	Refresher Unit Section	Inventory Test Item	Refresher Unit Section
1	21	16	5
2	10	17	27
3	19	18	8
4	18	19	24
5	9	20	29
6	3	21	28
7	6	22	16
8	20	23	4
9	17	24	26
10	7	25	1
11	13	26	23
12	14	27	15
13	30	28	25
14	12	29	22
15	11	30	2

Refresher Unit

---

1. The expression <u>because of</u>: *The meeting was delayed because of the bad weather.*

Use **because of** before a noun or noun phrase. Include an appropriate adjective if necessary to make the meaning clear.

> *We stayed up because of the movie on TV.*
> *Paul missed his plane because of the heavy traffic.*

Exercise 1: For each statement, ask a question using <u>why</u> and answer it with <u>because of</u> followed by a noun.

1. Jane likes her science class because she enjoys doing the experiments.
   Why does Jane like her science class?
   Because of the experiments.

2. Harry enjoys his philosophy class because he likes his teacher.
   <u>why does harry enjoy his philosophy class</u>?
   <u>Because of the teacher.</u>

3. Anne didn't go the beach because it was raining.
   <u>Why Anne didn't go to the beach</u>?
   <u>Because of the rain</u>

4. Peter couldn't go to school because he had a high fever.
   <u>Why peter missed the school</u>?
   <u>Because of the fever.</u>

5. Allen was absent from work because of a family problem.
   <u>Why Allen was absent from work</u>?
   <u>because of a family problem</u>

6. The factory will be closed this afternoon because there was a fire in the laboratory.
   <u>Why the factory will be close this afternoon</u>?
   <u>Because of the fire</u>

2. To-infinitive phrases of purpose: *Why does Bill go out so much? To have fun.*

Use the **to**-infinitive to express purpose or reason. Put the **to**-infinitive at the beginning of short answers.

> *My brother borrowed money to buy a bicycle.*
> *Why did he want a bicycle?*
> *To get some exercise.*

Exercise 2: Fill in the blanks with the to-infinitive of one of the verbs given.

get	look
avoid	lose
fit	feel

1. My brother started walking to work _____*to get*_____ some exercise.
2. He needs the exercise __*to lose*__ weight.
3. His doctor told him to eat less __*to avoid*__ heart trouble.
4. My brother's doing it mainly __*to look*__ better.
5. But he's also concerned about his appearance. So he's eating less __*to get*__ better, and __*To fit*__ better into his clothes.

3. Use of very and too: *She's too short to reach the top shelf.*

Use **very** and **too** before adjectives and adverbs. **Very** means "a large amount or degree." **Too** means "an excessive amount or degree."

> *This cake is very beautiful, almost too beautiful to eat.*

Exercise 3: Fill in the blanks with very or too.

1. Mexico City is __*very*__ high above sea level.
2. The air is _____ thin.
3. During the 1972 Olympic Games, many athletes were afraid it was __*too*__ thin for them to perform __*very*__ well.
4. They arrived early and trained __*very*__ carefully at first.
5. Later they realized they had worried __*too*__ much about the thinness of the air.
6. They returned home __*very*__ pleased with their experiences in Mexico.

4. Use of enough: *Bob isn't tall enough to play basketball.*

Use **enough** before nouns, and after adjectives and adverbs. **Enough** means "adequate" or "sufficient."

> *The ideal city is small enough to be friendly and has enough attractions to be interesting.*

Exercise 4: Answer each question. Use the word in parentheses and enough.

1. Why is Mr. Coleman still in the hospital?   (well)
   Because he had a serious heart attack and he still isn't __*well*__ __*enough*__ to go home.
2. Why is Mrs. Coleman worried?   (nurses)
   Because the hospital doesn't have __*enough*__ __*nurses*__ .
3. Why doesn't Mr. Coleman like the taste of the food at the hospital?   (salt)
   Because they don't put _____ _____ in it.
4. Why can't Mrs. Coleman prepare special food for her husband?   (time)
   Because she works and doesn't have _____ _____ .
5. Why is Mrs. Coleman working overtime?   (money)
   Because she doesn't have _____ _____ to pay the hospital bills.
6. Why didn't Mr. Coleman read the novels she brought him?   (interesting)
   Because they weren't _____ _____ .
7. Why do so many people die from heart attacks?   (soon)
   Because they don't get help _____ _____ .

5. And . . . too connecting two affirmative statements: *Mexico is in North America and Canada is too.*

Use **and . . . too** to connect two affirmative statements. To avoid repetition, use only the auxiliary. In the second part, the auxiliary always occurs in the uncontracted form.

> *Joseph speaks Japanese and Yoko does too.*
> *We've met the new boss and they have too.*

Exercise 5: Complete the sentences according to the example.

1. Colombia is north of the Equator and Venezuela __*is*__ __*too*__ .
2. Colombia is mountainous and Venezuela _____ _____ .
3. Colombia has grown coffee for a long time and Venezuela _____ _____ .

11

4. Colombia will probably continue to do so and Venezuela _____ _____ .
5. Columbia exports a lot of its coffee and many other countries _____ _____ .
6. Venezuela consumes most of its coffee internally and Puerto Rico _____
_____ .

---

6. And . . . either to connect two negative statements: *Mathematics isn't easy to learn, and languages aren't either.*

Use **and . . . either** to connect two negative statements. To avoid repetition in the second part, use an auxiliary with a negative.

> *Mexico isn't an island and Germany isn't either.*
> *You aren't asleep and no one else here is either.*

Exercise 6: Complete the sentences according to the example.

1. Edith can't remember names. I can't remember names.
   Edith can't remember names and I can't either.
2. My sister won't go skiing. My mother won't go skiing.

   _____ .
3. Mary shouldn't work too long. Albert shouldn't work too long.

   _____ .
4. Toshi doesn't drive a car. Annette doesn't drive a car.

   _____ .
5. Yoko isn't here. Her friends aren't here.

   _____ .
6. I can't go out tonight. Francis can't go out tonight.

   _____ .

---

7. But connecting an affirmative and a negative statement: *Many high school students want to go to college, but Frank Brown doesn't.*

Use **but** to connect an affirmative and a negative statement. To avoid repetition in the second part, use an auxiliary or a shortened form of the statement.

> *Aspirin is usually harmless, but sometimes it isn't.*
> *I don't like to take aspirin, but sometimes I have to.*

Exercise 7: Complete the sentences as in the examples.

1. Barbara is from California. Anna isn't from California.
   Barbara is from California, but Anna isn't.

2. Barbara has to move to Chicago, but she doesn't want to move to Chicago.
   Barbara has to move to Chicago, but she doesn't want to.
3. Victor was born in Detroit. John wasn't born in Detroit.

   _____ .
4. Victor isn't an auto mechanic. John is an auto mechanic.

   _____ .
5. Lucy took a trip to Puerto Rico. Rosemary didn't want to take a trip to Puerto Rico.

   _____ .
6. Lucy can speak fluent Spanish. Rosemary can't speak fluent Spanish.

   _____ .

8. **It in subject position for a delayed to-infinitive:** *It's difficult to play the piano well.*

Use **it** to fill the subject position when a **to**-infinitive subject is placed later in the sentence.

> *It's impossible to overestimate the importance of regular exercise.*

Exercise 8: Rewrite the sentences below, using it and a to-infinitive.

1. Staying healthy is important.
   It's important to stay healthy.
2. Eating wisely is essential.

   _____ .
3. Dieting is sometimes necessary.

   _____ .
4. Exercising regularly can help.

   _____ .
5. Remaining healthy without good habits is impossible.

   _____ .
6. Getting enough sleep is helpful.

   _____ .

9. **It in the subject position for a delayed to-infinitive introduced by a for phrase:** *It's difficult for a blind person to travel alone.*

Use the **for** phrase with the delayed **to**-infinitive when the subject of the infinitive is important to the meaning of the sentence.

> *In a big city, it's important for people to be careful.*

Exercise 9: Rewrite the following sentences using the word(s) in parentheses. Use _it_, a _for_ phrase, and a _to_-infinitive.

1. Meteorologists cannot easily predict the weather.   (difficult)
   It is difficult for meteorologists to predict the weather.
2. They need to gather information.   (necessary)
   _____ .
3. They have to consider all the facts.   (important)
   _____ .
4. They have to weigh the different factors.   (a difficult task)
   _____ .
5. People expect perfect predictions.   (a mistake)
   _____ .
6. Meteorologists make mistakes.   (easy)
   _____ .

10. The -ing form of the verb as subject: *Riding a bicycle is good exercise.*

You can use the **-ing** form of the verb as the subject of a sentence.
   Learning a second language is an accomplishment.

Exercise 10: Make sentences like the models. Use the -ing form as the subject.

1. It's relaxing to fish.
   Fishing is relaxing.
2. It requires talent to write poetry.
   _____ .
3. It's good exercise to run.
   _____ .
4. It's enjoyable to ice-skate.
   _____ .
5. It's fun to tell jokes.
   _____ .
6. It takes intelligence and patience to play chess.
   _____ .

11. Quantifiers as noun substitutes: *The people in most of the countries of South America speak Spanish.*

Quantifiers may be either singular (**one, none, either (one), neither (one), everyone, any one, no one**) or plural (**all, both, some, several, a few, many, most, twenty, few, none**).

> *I told my parents I was leaving home. Neither of them was pleased. In fact, both of them were quite upset.*

None can take a singular or plural verb. **A few** means "a small number—about 3 or 4." **Few** means "only a very small number—a lot less than one might expect."

> *There were a few positions available in the company. Many people applied, but few of them were qualified.*

Quantifiers can occur alone as subjects or with **of** + a noun or pronoun. The **of** phrase can be omitted when the context makes it clear.

> *Many of my friends speak Spanish. Most of them are from Mexico but some are from Puerto Rico.*

Everyone, anyone, and **no one** are not followed by **of.**

> *Everyone seemed happy.*

Exercise 11: Fill in the blanks with the appropriate quantifier listed below.

both	few
all	a few
no one	most

1. Although the U.S. and Germany are not usually thought of as nations where farmers have an important role, ____*both*____ of these countries depend heavily on their farmers and on the crops they produce.
2. In fact, _____ of the industrial countries would be in very serious financial trouble if _____ of the crops which are grown for export were discontinued.
3. _____ should underestimate the importance of agriculture.
4. _____ events in history have brought about more harmful results than agricultural failure.
5. And _____ of the countries of the world owe much of their wealth to the money received from the sale of their farm products.

12. The infinitive as the object of a verb: *The hikers watched the sun go down.*

The subject of the infinitive is expressed when it is different from that of the verb.
Use the object form of the pronoun for the subject of the infinitive. The infinitive
without **to** occurs after the verbs **make** (meaning "force"), **have** (meaning "causing
to happen"), **let** (meaning "to permit"), and several verbs of perceiving: **watch, see,
hear, listen to, notice, observe.**

> *Mary helped her brother bake a cake.*
> *Mother made us wash the dishes.*
> *Father had the tailor make him a suit.*
> *Don't let the light go out.*
> *She watched her grandmother make bread.*

Exercise 12: Combine the sentences using the infinitive.

1. Grandmother prepared dinner. We watched.
   We watched grandmother prepare dinner.
2. I set the table. Mother made me.

   _____ .

3. John tasted the soup. Grandmother let him.

   _____ .

4. He cut the meat. Grandfather helped him.

   _____ .

5. The visitors came in. We heard them.

   _____ .

6. The visitors put their coats in the bedroom. We saw them.

   _____ .

13. The use of the <u>to</u>-infinitive after certain verbs: *The robbery victims didn't expect to escape alive.*

With the verbs **try, learn, hope, plan, intend, expect,** and **forget,** the
to-infinitive is used without a subject.

> *Cecilia intends to go to sleep soon.*

After the verbs **tell, advise, permit,** and **force,** the **to**-infinitive is always used with
an expressed subject. If the expressed subject is a pronoun, the object form is used.

> *Cecilia told Sarah to go home.*
> *Cecilia advised me to go home too.*

After **want, ask,** and **expect,** the **to**-infinitive is used without a subject if the subject of the infinitive and the main verb are the same, and with an expressed subject if they are different.

> *I want to leave now.*
> *I want her to leave with me.*

Exercise 13: Combine each pair of sentences using the to-infinitive.

1. We visited the city of Washington. We planned to.
   We planned to visit the city of Washington.
2. We studied the map of Washington. We tried to.
   _____ .

3. We asked a police officer. John advised us to.
   _____ .

4. The police officer directed us. We expected him to.
   _____ .

5. We followed his directions. The police officer told us to.
   _____ .

6. We saw the Air and Space Museum. We wanted to.
   _____ .

14. Adjectives with the to-infinitive: *Sarah seemed anxious to get home early.*

You can use the **to**-infinitive with adjectives that express emotional states: **afraid, anxious, careful, certain, content, eager, fortunate, glad, happy, impatient, likely, lucky, pleased, proud, ready, sorry,** and **sure.** These adjectives follow the verbs **be, feel, seem, look, appear,** and **sound.**

> *Joseph seemed happy to be home.*
> *Carol was delighted to see him.*
> *Joseph looked eager to tell about his trip to Peru.*

Exercise 14: Combine each pair of sentences as in the example.

1. We're anxious. We want to leave soon.
   We're anxious to leave soon.
2. Maria seems ready. She'll drive us to the airport.
   _____ .

3. Tom feels happy. He'll be away for two weeks.
   _____ .

4. Linda looks impatient. She wants to leave right away.

   _____ .

5. Nicholas is glad. He'll visit his friend in Washington.

   _____ .

6. Everyone is eager. They want to arrive at the airport on time.

   _____ .

---

15. The -ing form of the verb as object: *A sick person should not postpone seeing the doctor.*

The -**ing** form of the verb can be used as the object of certain verbs such as **avoid, enjoy, mind, suggest, admit, consider, deny, finish, imagine, miss, postpone, practice, recommend,** and **report.**
   If you don't mind working hard, you might enjoy working in a restaurant.

Exercise 15: Combine each pair of sentences as in the example.

1. We felt hungry. We admitted it.
   We admitted feeling hungry.
2. We went to Nicole's new restaurant. John suggested it.

   _____ .

3. Margaret found an inexpensive cafeteria. Margaret reported it.

   _____ .

4. Everyone preferred to go to Nicole's. Everyone admitted it.

   _____ .

5. We ordered our favorite foods. We enjoyed it.

   _____ .

6. We didn't leave until the restaurant closed. We postponed it.

   _____ .

---

16. The to-infinitive or the -ing form of the verb as object: *After the last note of the symphony, the audience started clapping loudly.*

The verbs **begin, continue, hate, hesitate, like, love, prefer, start,** and **try** can be used with either the **to**-infinitive or the -**ing** form of the verb.
   If you begin living more simply, you may begin to enjoy life more.

Exercise 16: Complete the sentences using the words in parentheses. First, give the -ing form of the verb. Then give the to-infinitive.

1. Pedro likes _____ *driving* _____ . (drive)
   I like _____ *to drive* _____ too.
2. Sylvia prefers _____ . (play basketball)
   and Linda prefers _____ too.
3. Walter and John started _____ . (discuss politics)
   I started _____ too.
4. Everyone tried _____ the others. (convince)
   They tried _____ me, too.
5. I hate _____ . (argue about politics)
   Do you hate _____ , too?
6. John loves _____ . (talk about science fiction)
   Does Anita love _____ , too?

---

17. The past perfect tense: *By 1930, silent films had been replaced by talking pictures.*

The past perfect tense expresses a past time occurring before another past time. Form the past perfect tense with **had** and the past participle of the main verb. The negative is formed with **hadn't.** The contraction of **had** is **'d.**

Already, just, and adverbs of frequency like **never** are usually placed between **had** and the past participle.

> *Mary was very upset when she caught the flu. She'd never been so ill before. She'd had colds, but she hadn't ever felt so weak.*

Exercise 17: Complete the sentences with the past or past perfect form of the verb in parentheses.

1. Last week I _____ *watched* _____ (watch) them tear down an old medical building on Hunter Street. It was something I _____ *had never seen* _____ (never, see) before.
2. It _____ offices for doctors and dentists for fifty years. (provide)
3. The owners _____ (tear) it down because it _____ (become) too expensive to keep in repair.

4. Many people _____ (protest) before the owners _____
   the final decision.   (make)
5. By week's end, the heavy steel ball _____ (reduce) the building to a
   heap of debris.
6. When I _____ (go) back to Hunter Street today, they
   _____ (already, take) all of the old bricks away.

---

18. A series of adjectives as modifiers of a noun: *Driving a nice Italian car is
    enjoyable.*

Determiners are placed before adjectives. General adjectives usually precede other
adjectives in a series. They are followed by adjectives of size, age, color, and
nationality, in that order. Commas are often placed between adjectives, especially
when they are adjectives of the same category.

> *There's a nice new Japanese restaurant on Main Street.*
> *They have nice, soft music there.*

**Exercise 18: Complete the sentences with the words given in parentheses.
Be sure to put the words in the correct order.**

1. Tokyo is _____*a big, modern, Japanese*_____ city.
   (Japanese, a, modern, big)
2. Mr. Lopez owns _____ car.
   (black, German, a, large)
3. The Concorde is _____ jet.
   (a, European, large, new)
4. A beaver has _____ fur.
   (brown, soft, short)
5. Mary's pet is _____ dog.
   (black, a, French, small)
6. Anita lives in _____ house.
   (white, a, old, little)

---

19. A series of nouns as modifiers of a noun: *The store was having a winter hat
    sale.*

A series of nouns can modify another noun.

> *My cousin is a member of the secret service police.*

Exercise 19: Rearrange the words to complete the sentences.

1. A police station is the headquarters of _____*a local police force*_____ .
   (local, a, force, police)

2. _____ is a car usually equipped with radio telephone
   devices.   (a, car, patrol, police)

3. _____ is a dog specially trained to assist the
   police.   (police, a, dog)

4. _____ help tourists.   (the, officers, patrol, highway)

5. _____ patrol the subway.   (officers, the, police,
   transit, city)

6. _____ tries to prevent drug trafficking.   (city,
   squad, narcotics, the)

---

20. Adverbs as modifiers of nouns: *The dinner was excellent, and the dance*
   afterwards was fun.

Adverbial expressions of place and time may occur after a noun to modify it. The
adverb may be a single word or a prepositional phrase.
   The discussion before the meeting was worthwhile.
   The people there were very friendly.

**Exercise 20: Combine the sentences as in the example. Use the adverb as
a modifier of the noun.**

1. There's a man next to Mrs. Herman. The man is a noise pollution expert.
   The man *next to Mrs. Herman is a noise pollution expert.*

2. They had a conversation today. Their conversation was about airport noises.
   Their conversation _____ _____ .

3. One of Mrs. Herman's offices is near the airport. The office is unpleasant.
   Her office _____ .

4. There are planes nearby. The planes are noisy.
   The planes _____ .

5. There's noise during the summer months. The noise seems louder.
   The noise _____ .

6. There have been protests there. The protests have been serious.
   The protests _____ .

21. The passive construction: *Many trees have been attacked by disease in recent years.*

The object of an active sentence becomes the subject of a passive sentence. The subject of an active sentence sometimes becomes the object of the preposition **by** in the passive sentence. It is called a "passive agent." The passive form of a verb consists of the same tense of the verb **be** + the past participle of the verb.

      Active: *Robert wrote a letter.*
      Passive: *A letter was written by Robert.*

Exercise 21: Change these sentences to the passive.

1. The Tennis Club is giving a picnic.
   A picnic is being given by the Tennis Club.
2. Doris DeSio is setting the tables.

   _____ .

3. Jim Johnson has fixed a large salad.

   _____ .

4. Linda and George Bond have brought roast beef.

   _____ .

5. Alice Coleman baked apple pies.

   _____ .

6. Bill Forest will serve coffee and tea.

   _____ .

22. The passive construction without an agent: *Many tons of paper are used for newspapers every day.*

The agent in a passive sentence is often left out when it is clear from the context, or when it is not known.

    Many new products have been introduced since World War II.

Exercise 22: Complete the sentences using the correct passive form of the verbs in parentheses.

1. The electric light _____ *was invented* _____ in 1879.   (invent)

2. Our policy _____ tomorrow.   (announce)
3. Gold _____ for more than $600 an ounce in 1979.   (sell)
4. Lower food prices _____ now.   (need)
5. The patient _____ from the hospital next month.   (release)
6. Babe Ruth _____ to the Baseball Hall of Fame in 1936.   (elect)

---

23. Adjectives ending in -ing and -ed: *Photography is a fascinating hobby.*

Adjectives ending in **-ing** have the meaning of "causing a reaction or feeling."
Adjectives ending in **-ed** refer to "experiencing a reaction or feeling."
> *The discouraged ball players lost the game.*
> *The spectators thought it was a disappointing performance.*

Exercise 23: Fill in the blanks with the appropriate ending, either -ing or -ed.

1. There are scientists who are interest_ed_ in exploring the oceans.
2. These professors have given fascinat_____ descriptions about the marvelous plant and animal life existing in the seas.
3. Their appeal_____ reports and photos of deep sea life continue to attract interest_____ audiences.
4. People are very surpris_____ at the variety of fish observed, and at the amaz_____ behavior.

---

24. The order of ordinal and cardinal numbers: *The first two guests to arrive were Alice and Bob.*

Ordinal numbers, such as **first, second,** and **third** precede cardinal numbers like **one, two** and **three. Next** and **last** act like ordinal numbers, while quantity expressions like **few** act like cardinal numbers.
> *In the last few years the pace of life has increased.*

Exercise 24: Complete the sentences below with cardinal and ordinal numbers according to the information given.

	Fares	Subway Stations	Travel Time
1.	45¢	Eastern Market⟷Gallery Place	17 min.
2.	45¢	Silver Spring⟷Gallery Place	17 min.
3.	45¢	Crystal City⟷Virginia Square	17 min.
4.	50¢	Silver Spring⟷Visitor's Center	14 min.
5.	55¢	Courthouse⟷Crystal City	14 min.
6.	45¢	Visitor's Center⟷Gallery Place	3 min.
7.	45¢	Courthouse⟷Virginia Square	3 min.
8.	35¢	Minnesota Avenue⟷Stadium	3 min.
9.	55¢	Minnesota Avenue⟷Visitor's Center	27 min.
10.	90¢	Minnesota Avenue⟷Courthouse	27 min.
11.	90¢	Stadium⟷Virginia Square	27 min.

1. The fare between the ___*first*___ ___*three*___ subway stations is 45¢.
2. The fare between the _____ _____ subway stations is 90¢.
3. The travel time between the _____ _____ subway stations is 17 minutes.
4. The travel time between the _____ _____ subway stations is 14 minutes.
5. The travel time between _____ _____ subway stations is 3 minutes.
6. The travel time between the _____ _____ subway stations is 27 minutes.

---

25. The order of numbers and other adjectives: *Some libraries save only the two most recent copies of a book.*

Numbers usually precede other adjectives. Numbers are often used with comparatives and superlatives. The noun can be replaced by **one** or **ones** to avoid repetition.
   We don't need five new ideas. We need one good one.

Exercise 25. Using the information given below, complete each sentence with the number and the superlative form of the adjective given in parentheses.

	Fares	Subway Stations	Travel Time
1.	45¢	Crystal City⟷Airport	2 minutes
2.	60¢	Crystal City⟷Eastern Market	26 minutes

3.	60¢	Crystal City⟷Gallery Place	21 minutes
4.	80¢	Crystal City⟷Minnesota Avenue	22 minutes
5.	$1.25	Crystal City⟷Silver Spring	38 minutes
6.	70¢	Crystal City⟷Stadium	30 minutes
7.	60¢	Crystal City⟷Visitor's Center	24 minutes
8.	60¢	Crystal City⟷Virginia Square	17 minutes
9.	55¢	Crystal City⟷Courthouse	14 minutes

1. The ____three____ ____longest____ travel times are 38, 30, and 26 minutes.   (long, three)
2. The _____ _____ travel times are 2 and 14 minutes.   (short, two)
3. The _____ _____ fares are 45¢ and 55¢.   (low, two)
4. The _____ _____ fares are $1.25, 80¢, and 70¢.   (three, high)
5. The _____ _____ travel times are also the least expensive.   (brief, two)

---

26. Sentences with an <u>if</u> condition: *Taking photographs is easy if you are careful.*

Use **if** to connect a condition to the main clause. The present tense is used in the main clause and in the **if** condition to talk about things that are generally true. When the **if** condition precedes the main clause, separate it with a comma.

Land is good for agriculture if the soil is rich and if it gets sufficient sun and rain.
If you throw a ball up in the air, it comes down.

Exercise 26: Complete the following sentences using the verbs in parentheses.

1. If you ____heat____ something, it generally ____increases____ in size.   (heat, increase)
2. If there _____ sufficient rainfall, plants _____ rapidly.   (be, grow)
3. If the nights _____ very long for half the year, the days _____ very long during the other half.   (be, be)
4. If you _____ economics, you generally _____ to study statistics too.   (study, have)
5. A fire _____ out if there _____ no oxygen.   (go, be)
6. If a table _____ the shape of a square, its sides _____ all the same size.   (have, be)

27. Sentences with an <u>if</u> condition in the present tense and a main clause in the future tense: *If we don't control pollution, we won't be able to live on earth.*

The future tense is used in the main clause to talk about specific things that will happen if a certain condition is met. When the future tense is used in the main clause, the present tense is used in the **if** condition.

> *If there is a shortage of gasoline, the price will certainly go up.*

Exercise 27: Fill in the blanks with the proper tense of the verbs in parentheses.

1. If the price of coffee _____*continues*_____ to go up, many people _____*will stop*_____ buying it.   (continue, stop)
2. If they _____ buying coffee, they _____ to drink something else.   (stop, have)
3. Some people _____ water if they _____ an acceptable substitute.   (drink, not find)
4. If a person _____ plain water, he _____ to add something to it.   (not like, try)
5. If he _____ enough, some new drink _____ .   (experiment, be made)
6. But if he _____ to create something new, he _____ whatever is available.   (not be able, drink)

28. Contrary-to-fact conditional sentences in the present tense: *If fewer people drove to work, there would be less pollution.*

To form contrary-to-fact conditional sentences in the present, use the conditional **would** (or **could**) and the simple form of the verb in the main clause. Use the past tense in the **if** clause. **Were** is usually preferred to **was** with **I, he, she,** and **it** in the **if** clause. The contraction of **would** is **'d.**

> *If I were you, I'd study first and play later.*

Exercise 28: Fill in the blanks with the proper tense of the verbs in parentheses.

1. If I _____*were*_____ rich, I _____*'d take*_____ a trip around the world.   (be, take)

2. If Mary _____ some money, she _____ new clothes.   (have, buy)
3. If Vincent _____ harder, he _____ a job.   (try, find)
4. If the weather _____ better, Anne _____ mountain climbing.   (be, go)
5. If we _____ a longer vacation, we _____ throughout Europe.   (have, travel)
6. If I _____ you, I _____ computer science.   (be, study)

---

29. Sentences with time clauses: *While Toshi was studying in Rome, he visited many famous monuments.*

When, while, after and **before** express time relations between two clauses. **While** introduces an action which is in progress at the time of the main clause.

> *While a lecturer is speaking, an audience should be quiet.*

When introduces an action that takes place at the same time as the action in the main clause.

> *When spring comes, everyone breathes more easily.*

If the time clause precedes the main clause, it is separated from it by a comma.

Exercise 29: Complete the sentences with the appropriate form of the verbs given in parentheses.

1. When Maria _____*saw*_____ the unusual appearance of the sky, she _____*turned on*_____ the radio.   (see, turn on)
2. While _____ the weather report, Maria _____ the business news.   (wait for, listen to)
3. When the weatherman _____ the various conditions controlling the weather, Maria _____ concerned.   (explain, become)
4. While Maria _____ to the local news, she _____ announcements about swollen rivers.   (listen, hear)
5. After Maria _____ the radio, she _____ to call up her mother.   (turn off, decide)
6. While she _____ to her mother, the sky _____ darker and heavy rain _____ to fall outside.   (talk, become, begin)

30. The use of the verbs <u>make</u> and <u>do</u>: *I have to make breakfast every morning.*

Make and **do** have several meanings. **Make** can mean "to construct or produce something, either a physical object or a condition."

> *John made a kite last March.*
> *His new kite made a good impression on everyone.*

Make can mean "to cause to become."

> *Mary always makes her family happy.*

Make can mean "to cause someone to do something."

> *Mother made Rosemary take music lessons.*

Do can mean "to perform some action."

> *What are you doing tonight?*

Do can mean "to perform a procedure."

> *I do my homework after dinner.*

Exercise 30: Use <u>make</u> and <u>do</u> appropriately in the spaces provided.

1. **Phyllis:** Let's ___*make*___ coffee first and ___*do*___ the cleaning later.
2. **Jane:** If we _____ our best, we'll _____ progress quickly.

3. **Alice:** Have you _____ any new friends recently?
4. **Bob:** I think so. I try _____ something nice for someone everyday.
5. **Alice:** That must _____ you feel good.

Inventory Test 2

Check the box next to the word which correctly completes the statement or question.

Example: All the work on the project has been _____ by our staff.
- [ ] a. to finish
- [x] b. finished
- [ ] c. finish
- [ ] d. finishing

1. Martha thinks Craig is quite _____ .
- [ ] a. charm
- [ ] b. charming
- [ ] c. charmed
- [ ] d. charms

2. Alice has been to South America and _____ .
- [ ] a. I have
- [ ] b. I've too
- [ ] c. I have too
- [ ] d. so I have

3. The electric light bulb _____ about a century ago.
- [ ] a. invented
- [ ] b. was inventing
- [ ] c. was invented
- [ ] d. has invented

4. If you live downtown, many things are _____ to walk to.
- [ ] a. enough close
- [ ] b. close enough
- [ ] c. too close
- [ ] d. more close

5. The _____ was quite successful.
- [ ] a. last week meeting
- [ ] b. last meeting week
- [ ] c. meeting last week
- [ ] d. meeting week last

6. _____ the states of the U.S. are separated from the others.
- [ ] a. Two of
- [ ] b. Two
- [ ] c. Some
- [ ] d. One of

7. If people exercised more, they _____ healthier.
- [ ] a. were
- [ ] b. 'll be
- [ ] c. 're
- [ ] d. 'd be

8. _____ sick is not pleasant.
- [ ] a. Be
- [ ] b. Being
- [ ] c. Was
- [ ] d. To being

9. A large picture is often more attractive than _____ .
☒ a. two small ones
☐ b. two small
☐ c. two smalls
☐ d. two ones small

10. They made us _____ our work early.
☐ a. finished
☐ b. finish
☐ c. finishing
☒ d. to finish

11. The restaurant is closed _____ fire.
☐ a. because of a
☐ b. because
☐ c. for a
☐ d. for

12. Many people _____ at the airport before the famous flier landed.
☐ a. gather
☐ b. will gather
☐ c. had gathered
☐ d. have gathered

13. I really have done _____ at work.
☐ a. a lot of progress
☐ b. a good job
☐ c. a good impression
☐ d. a lot of coffee

14. Since Jane moved to Los Angeles, she has done _____ well.
☐ a. too
☐ b. very
☐ c. enough
☐ d. more

15. A political candidate cannot avoid _____ difficult questions.
☐ a. answering
☐ b. to answer
☐ c. answer
☐ d. from answering

16. The club called a meeting _____ elect a new president.
☐ a. to
☐ b. by
☐ c. for
☐ d. of

17. A photographer is often impatient _____ his film.
☐ a. develop
☐ b. to develop
☐ c. for developing
☐ d. by developing

18. We all stood up when the guest of honor _____ the room.
☐ a. enters
☐ b. had entered
☐ c. has entered
☐ d. entered

19. After the curtain went down, the audience continued _____ for 5 minutes.
☐ a. shout
☐ b. for shouting
☐ c. by shouting
☐ d. to shout

20. _____ stay home this afternoon if it rains.
☐ a. I
☐ b. I'll
☐ c. I'd
☐ d. I had

21. It's usually necessary for an engineer _____ reports.
☐ a. writing
☐ b. for writing
☐ c. write
☐ d. to write

22. If I have a cold, I usually _____ medicine.
☐ a. would take
☐ b. take
☐ c. took
☐ d. had taken

23. The students decided _____ a play.
☒ a. give
☐ b. to give
☐ c. giving
☐ d. gave

24. _____ pages of a book usually contain an index.
☐ a. The few last
☒ b. Few last
☐ c. Last few
☐ d. The last few

25. Iowa gets a lot of snow, but Florida _____ .
☐ a. doesn't
☐ b. doesn't get
☐ c. does too
☐ d. doesn't either

26. The visitors drank from _____ .
☐ a. coffee cups plastic
☐ b. plastic coffee cups
☐ c. cups plastic coffee
☐ d. plastic cups coffee

27. Animals cannot live without water, and plants _____ .
☐ a. can
☐ b. can too
☐ c. can't either
☐ d. can't

28. All the food _____ by the guests.
☐ a. was eaten
☐ b. ate
☐ c. was eating
☐ d. eat

29. It's always interesting _____ people from abroad.
☐ a. to meeting
☐ b. meet
☐ c. we meet
☐ d. to meet

30. _____ wine is a good gift for a friend.
☐ a. An old fine red
☐ b. A fine old red
☐ c. A red fine old
☐ d. A fine red old

Reference Key for Inventory Test 2

If you missed any items on Inventory Test 2, locate the number of each item on the list below and study the corresponding section in the Refresher Unit.

Inventory Test Item	Refresher Unit Section	Inventory Test Item	Refresher Unit Section
1	23	16	2
2	5	17	14
3	22	18	29
4	4	19	16
5	20	20	27
6	11	21	9
7	28	22	26
8	10	23	13
9	25	24	24
10	12	25	7
11	1	26	19
12	17	27	6
13	30	28	21
14	3	29	8
15	15	30	18

Unit 1

Complete

Jason Shell is waiting to _____ the bus to _____ . A couple is standing ____
line at the bus _____ . Jason recognizes them ____ the people who _____ just
moved into the house _____ the street from _____ . Since he hasn't met
them _____ , he decides to _____ himself.

Jason: Excuse ____ . Aren't you the people _____ moved into _____ Wilsons'
old house?

Woman: _____ yes, we are.

Jason: _____ Jason Shell. I _____ in the blue house _____ the street
from _____ .

Woman: *(Extending her hand)* I'm Thelma Robards. How ____ you do?

Jason: *(Shaking her hand)* _____ do you do?

Man: And _____ Glen Robards. *(Shaking Jason's Hand)* _____ to
meet you.

Jason: Nice ____ meet you _____ . When did you move ____ ?

Glen: _____ Friday.

Jason: I thought someone might _____ moved in, because I saw a car in the
_____ when I got _____ from work. But then I
_____ notice any _____ Friday evening.

33

Thelma: We must have _____ at the shopping _____ .

Jason: You know, my wife and I _____ a party Friday night. If _____ known that you'd _____ in, we would _____ invited you.

Glen: That _____ have been nice.

Jason: And you could have _____ some people from the _____ . Well, here _____ the bus. It's _____ nice talking to _____ .

Glen: (*Shaking Jason's hand*) I hope _____ see you again soon.

Thelma: (*Shaking Jason's hand*) Yes, in fact, why _____ you and your wife come _____ for dinner tonight?

Jason: Thank you. I'd love _____ , and I'm sure my wife would too, _____ she's _____ other plans. I'll stop _____ right after work and let you know _____ sure.

Glen: Great. See you _____ .

Thelma: Good-bye, now.

Jason: _____ a good day.

Write

A. Write a contrary-to-fact conditional sentence for each question and answer below.

1. Why didn't you go out on Sunday? Because I felt tired.
   If I hadn't felt tired, I would have gone out on Sunday.

2. Why didn't you call last week? Because I lost your phone number.
   If I hadn't lost your phone number, I would have called last week.

3. Why didn't Janet take the job? Because they didn't offer her enough money.
   If she hadn't offered her enough money she would have taken the job.

4. Why did Francis drop out of school? Because he had to work full-time.
   If he hadn't had to work full-time he wouldn't have dropped out.

5. Why didn't the Shells invite the Robards to their party? Because they didn't know the Robards had moved in.
   If she had kown, The Robards had moved in she would have invited

6. Why didn't Jason accept the Robards' invitation immediately? Because he didn't know whether his wife could come.

had known, would have accepted

_____ .

B. Complete the following sentences according to your own experiences.

1. *(I go the dentist every year)* whether or not I want to.

2. _____

if I had a day off.

3. _____

whether or not I have enough money.

4. _I will go swimming_____

unless it rains.

5. _____

whether or not I feel like it.

6. _I will study for exams_____

if I have enough time this weekend.

7. Unless the economy improves significantly _many people have_

_to be layoff_____ .

8. If I were the mayor of my city _I would work full time_

(would lower Taxes

(would demolish old Houses

C. Write an appropriate comment on the following situations using <u>could have</u>, <u>should have</u>, or <u>shouldn't have</u>.

1. Mary hurt her back carrying a heavy typewriter by herself. (shouldn't have)
(She shouldn't have carried it by herself.)

2. Barbara didn't have a good time at the beach because the sun was too hot for her. (could have)

_she could have had_____ .

3. Anne stayed up until three and was so exhausted this morning that she could hardly work. (shouldn't have)

_____ .

4. Bob had a lot of free time last week, but he didn't finish his work. (should have)

_____ .

5. Pam did not enjoy herself at the party, but she stayed until very late. (could have)

_____ .

6. We missed the train because we left the house too late. (should have)

_____ .

7. Denise didn't do the math problems because she didn't understand them.   (could have)

_____.

8. Alfred got a fifty-dollar speeding ticket for driving twenty miles an hour over the speed limit.   (shouldn't have)

_____.

D. Give a possible explanation to respond to the following statements and/or questions. Use <u>might</u> or <u>might have</u>.

1. Where are my shoes? I know I took them off in the bedroom.
   (They might be under the bed.)
   (You might have put them in the closet.)
2. What happened to Alfred? He has a black eye.

_____.

3. Susan is absent from class again. She hasn't been here all week.

_____.

4. Oh dear! The front door is unlocked.

_____.

5. What's wrong with Jack? He hasn't said a word all evening.

_____.

6. I heard a lot of sirens outside last night, but I didn't get up to see what was going on.

_____.

E. Give a probable explanation in response to the following statements and/or questions. Use <u>must</u> or <u>must have</u>.

1. What's John doing here? I thought he'd gone skiing. Look! His leg is broken.
   (He must have broken it while he was skiing.)
2. What happened to the meat I left on the table? No one was home all day . . . except the dog.

_____.

3. Look! Bob's asleep. How could he fall asleep in such an interesting movie?

_____.

4. I've been dieting and I haven't had anything to eat all day.

_____.

5. Phyllis hasn't called for weeks. I can't understand why. . . . We had a little argument when we last spoke to each other, but I didn't think it was anything serious.

   _____.

6. Look, the Taylors' house is very quiet. All of the windows are closed and the shades are drawn. It's been like that for three weeks now.

   _____.

Listen

A. Listen carefully to the information. Then check the box next to the statement that is true according to the information you have heard.

1. ☐ a. I went skiing.
   ☐ b. I had a vacation and went skiing.
   ☐ c. I didn't have a vacation.

2. ☐ a. John called her.
   ☐ b. John didn't go to the dinner.
   ☐ c. John didn't call her.

3. ☐ a. She will work if you raise her salary.
   ☐ b. She will work if you don't raise her salary.
   ☐ c. She won't work even if you raise her salary.

4. ☐ a. He bought a big car.
   ☐ b. He was unable to buy a big car.
   ☐ c. He didn't buy a big car.

5. ☐ a. Marie is lost.
   ☐ b. It is possible that Marie left.
   ☐ c. Marie left for sure.

6. ☐ a. The businessman never calls back.
   ☐ b. The businessman didn't call back.
   ☐ c. The businessman called back.

B. Listen carefully to the brief dialogue, or part of a dialogue, and to the question that follows. Then check the box next to the correct answer.

1. ☐ a. One hour.
   ☐ b. About five more minutes.
   ☐ c. He should not call at all.

2. ☐ a. He enjoys their company.
   ☐ b. He wants to go to lunch with them.
   ☐ c. He doesn't enjoy being with them.

3. ☐ a. She won't pass the test.
   ☐ b. She won't be successful.
   ☐ c. She won't cheat.

4. ☐ a. Discouraged.
   ☐ b. Sick.
   ☐ c. Happy.

Vocabulary in Context

A. Complete the conversation between these two sisters using the appropriate idiom from the list below. Use contractions when possible.

had better   ought to   would rather

Alice: If you do badly in school, Mom and Dad will be furious.
You _____ not fail the exam tomorrow.

Margery: I know I should study. I _____ take out my books
right now and get to work, but I _____ watch TV.

B. Complete the sentences using the correct form of an appropriate expression from the list below.

get across	get along with	get on	get down
get ahead	get into	get off	get out of
get through with	get by	get in	

1. It's a pleasure to _____ your work and have time to spend with friends.
2. It isn't easy to _____ an idea to someone who isn't listening.
3. Don't let one difficult day _____ you _____ .
4. It's usually a waste of time and energy to _____ an argument about things that can't be changed.
5. It's helpful to try to _____ all kinds of people.
6. Most of us find that if we want to _____ at work, there's little time left for play.

38

7. When prices are high, you can hardly _____ , even when you've had a raise.
8. You should tell the driver your destination as soon as you _____ the taxi.
9. Usually you have to pay your fare right after you _____ the bus.
10. Your legs may feel strange after you _____ a horse.
11. When there's a fire, the fire fighters do their best to help people to _____ the building as quickly as possible.

Read

At a Concert, or a Dinner, Some People Just Doze Off

A.   The audience is enthralled. There's not a sound to be heard, other than the glorious music. But just a moment. Could it be? It could. It is.

The man in the fifth row is asleep, snoring, in fact. The woman beside him is jabbing her elbow into his ribs. Some of the neighbors are amused, others are irritated or horrified, but a surprising number of faces look sympathetic. Thank goodness, they seem to be saying, tonight at least, it's someone else.

Everyone knows someone who has fallen asleep in public, or continues to fall asleep in public, occasionally or frequently. Some sleepers are selective. They doze only at concerts, or at dinner parties, or at meetings, or in church. Others are indiscriminate. Any place is good enough, especially if it's a place they didn't want to be in the first place.

Sophia Loren, in her recent autobiography, noted that her husband, Carlo Ponti, would get to certain film premieres, promptly "drop off," and "I must then nervously try to keep him awake! Carlo! Carlo!" Miss Loren added that she wasn't annoyed by the napping; it had been a fact of life for such a long time that it amused her.

Check the box next to the correct answer.

1. An experience that most people have had is to _____ .
   - ☐ a. fall asleep in public
   - ☐ b. see someone fall asleep in public
   - ☐ c. snore at a concert

2. People who see someone fall asleep in public _____ .
   - ☐ a. are sometimes amused and sometimes annoyed
   - ☐ b. generally feel very irritated
   - ☐ c. always find the situation quite funny

3. Some people are _____ and thus will fall asleep anywhere.
   - ☐ a. sympathetic
   - ☐ b. indiscriminate
   - ☐ c. selective

4. When Sophia Loren says that her husband "drops off" in film premieres, she means that he _____ .
   - ☐ a. gets bored
   - ☐ b. takes a nap
   - ☐ c. becomes nervous

B.   Public sleepers are usually, but not always, men. The theory used to be that men were exhausted after a long day at the office, while women were at home eating chocolates and taking beauty naps. However, Margaret Thatcher and the late Golda Meir never were famous either for chocolate consumption or beauty naps. Thus, this theory is now advanced less often.

Jim Jensen, a television news correspondent who has, on occasion, fallen asleep in public, has two somewhat different theories. He thinks that women may be more conscious of good manners, and that they may also be more concerned with the way they look to others.

Mr. Jensen occasionally dozes at a meeting, and said, "I think I heard myself snoring in church once," but he admits that he, too, is conscious of a public image.

Foxy Carter, a retired Foreign Service officer, occasionally finds himself having a quiet nap at a dinner table. It usually happens when he's tired, and the hostess hasn't served dinner until 10 or 11 P.M.

"The kindest thing my date can do is give me a good swift kick in the shins," he said, and added, thoughtfully, "I've had some very good dates, very helpful in that way."

Perhaps the most unusual case of nodding off in public was experienced by William L. Winter. Mr. Winter is executive director of Assistance Dogs International, and is a frequent and popular lecturer. But one night:

"It was the weirdest feeling. I was lecturing, and I was putting myself to sleep. The audience was in good shape, and there I was, falling asleep."

But that's what friends are for—to observe heavy eyelids, and drooping heads, and imminent disaster, and—nudge, hard.

Check the box next to the correct answer.

1. The reason that public sleepers are usually men is probably because

   _____ .

   ☐ a. women take more beauty naps
   ☐ b. men are less conscious of good manners
   ☐ c. men get exhausted at work while women stay at home and relax

2. When Foxy Carter falls asleep at a dinner table he likes _____ .
   ☐ a. someone to kick him
   ☐ b. to keep on sleeping until 10 or 11 P.M.
   ☐ c. to be helpful to his date

3. A frequent and popular lecturer _____ .
   ☐ a. become annoyed when the audience fell asleep during his speech
   ☐ b. gave an unusual talk on dogs
   ☐ c. started to fall asleep while he was talking

4. Probably the nicest thing a friend can do for a public sleeper is to

   _____ .

   ☐ a. nudge the sleeper quite hard
   ☐ b. fall asleep at the same time
   ☐ c. watch the person's eyelids get heavy

Composition

A. A good paragraph usually contains a topic sentence (a sentence which states the main idea of the paragraph), some supporting sentences (examples, facts, opinions, statistics, etc.), and a conclusion. In the following paragraphs, identify the topic sentence (TS), the supporting sentences (SS), and the conclusion (C).

1. In these modern times we are used to a fast-paced life. (   ) We speed on highways that never end, or take planes to travel even faster. (   ) We eat in self-service restaurants to save time. (   ) We build machines to do our work as fast as possible, so that we can enjoy more leisure time. (   ) Then, in our leisure time, we are impatient because things move too slowly. (   )

2. The oldest dances developed as part of the primitive rituals once practice by all cultures. (   ) There were special dances to mark a birth, marriage, or death. (   ) Some dances accompanied the planting and harvesting of crops. (   ) Other dances served to praise the gods and to ask them to bring good fortune to the people. (   ) Even though most of these ritualistic dances have disappeared with the rise of modern civilization, dancing itself still remains popular throughout the world. (   )

B. Write a short paragraph according to the specifications given below. Begin with the topic sentence provided, and add supporting sentences and a conclusion.

Topic sentence: There are both advantages and disadvantages to living in the city.

Supporting sentences: Name two advantages and two disadvantages.

Conclusion: Explain why, in the end, you do or do not like living in the city.

_____
_____
_____
_____
_____
_____
_____
_____
_____

C. Write a paragraph about somebody you know who is either a very good or a very bad conversationalist. Start with one of the two topic sentences provided below. Then name the qualities (or faults) that make this person a good or a bad conversationalist. Finally, reach a conclusion about this person's conversational habits. You can find useful words and phrases in the textbook reading passage.

Topic sentence: (James) is an excellent conversationalist. Or: (James) is a terrible conversationalist.

_____
_____
_____
_____
_____
_____
_____
_____
_____
_____

Word Game

Try to find the words concealed in the puzzle. Find them by reading forward, backward, up, down, or diagonally—always in a straight line, with no letters omitted. Then complete the sentences below, using the appropriate expression with get. The first word has been circled.

get _____

```
h  a  i  n  t  o  b
e  g  y  u  r  g  a
f  b  u  d  n  i  h
a  c  r  o  s  s  e
h  m  l  w  r  o  a
t  a  o  n  i  h  d
n  o  f  f  o  u  t
```

1. I talked for two hours, but it was impossible to ___*get*___ anything ___*across*___ to him.
2. Ralph and Sue are on vacation and have enough money to _____ for only two more weeks.
3. They worked on Saturday and Sunday to _____ with the project.
4. Hurry up and _____ the car. If we don't leave now, we'll run into a lot of traffic.
5. Tom and Claire _____ arguments all the time; they just don't _____ .
6. To reach that address, you have to _____ this train.
7. Take it for three stops and _____ at 14th Street; then walk two blocks east.
8. Robert, _____ of bed. It's already 8:00 and you can't be late for school again.
9. When the weather is rainy and cold, it really _____ me _____ .

Unit 2

Complete

Nine-year-old Clay Larrabee's _____ has left home because his family is having _____ problems. Clay has found an _____ and has convinced _____ that it contains a _____ worth the money his _____ needs to get Clay's father to return _____ . Clay, his younger _____ Roxanna, and friend Greeley _____ come to Harry Van Dusen's _____ shop to see ____ the oyster has a pearl inside. Louis Wozzeck, the _____ watchmaker, and a writer from _____ of town, who has heard about Clay's _____ from the barber, are also inside the _____ .

Wozzeck:	What's this all _____ , Harry?
Harry:	I've _____ an oyster I want _____ to open.
Wozzeck:	That's what the kids have _____ telling me.
Roxanna:	*He* doesn't _____ there's a pearl in the oyster, _____ .
Wozzeck:	____ course, not! _____ foolishness!
Clay:	_____ a *big* pearl in it.
Wozzeck:	O.K., give me the _____ . I'll open it. Expert _____ repairer, to open an oyster!
Harry:	How much is a big pearl _____ , Louis?
Wozzeck:	Oh, a hundred. Two hundred, _____ .

Harry: A very big _____ ?

Wozzeck: Three, maybe.

Writer: I've looked _____ that oyster, and I'd _____ to buy it. How _____ do you want for it?

Clay: I don't _____ .

Writer: How _____ three hundred dollars?

Greeley: Three hundred dollars?

Clay: Is it _____ right, Mr. Van Dusen?

Harry: Sure, it's all _____ .

Clay: But _____ there ain't a pearl in it?

Writer: There _is,_ though.

Wozzeck: _____ you want to open _____ first?

Writer: No, I want the _____ thing. I don't think the pearl's stopped _____ .

Clay: He _____ there _is_ a pearl in _____ oyster, Mr. Van Dusen.

Harry: I think there _____ , too, Clay; so why _____ you just go on _____ and give the _____ to your mother?

Clay: Well. . . . I _knew_ I _____ going to find _____ good today!

Wozzeck: Three hundred _____ ! How do you _____ there's a pearl in it?

Writer: As far as I'm _____ , the whole thing's a pearl.

Write

A. Answer the questions using reflexive pronouns.

1. Who paid for you at the restaurant?
   I paid for myself.

2. Who did she buy those flowers for?

   _____ .

3. Who does Dick work for?

   _____ .

4. Who were you talking to a minute ago?

   _____ .

5. Who are you and Alice making that cake for?

   _____ .

6. Who taught your children to play chess?

   _____ .

7. Who will take care of us when we're old?

   _____ .

8. Who dresses your son for school in the morning?

   _____ .

B. Fill in the appropriate reflexive pronouns.

1. If you want a job to be well done, you sometimes have to do it
   _____*yourself*_____ .
2. I _____ don't know when he'll be arriving, but someone else
   probably does.
3. The house _____ is very large, but the garden is small.
4. The bosses _____ couldn't do that job, so why should they expect us
   to?
5. I know you could use some help with this, but there's a lot you two could do
   _____ to speed up the work.
6. He _____ is very capable, but I don't trust the other people who
   work with him.
7. Deborah built that table _____ .
8. He wanted to send his assistant over to help us, but I asked if he could come
   _____ .
9. We couldn't find anyone to fix the plumbing, so we had to do it
   _____ .
10. I can't convince Sarah to come with us. Why don't you talk to her
    _____ ?

C. Write request sentences for the following situations. Include words such as <u>everybody</u>, <u>somebody</u>, <u>anybody</u>, <u>you</u>, <u>let's</u>, <u>do</u>, <u>no</u>, and <u>please</u> when appropriate.

1. Alan and Jill are talking on the phone long distance. Alan is coming to Jill's city
   soon and she wants him to give her a call when he arrives. She says, "*Do give me
   a call when you arrive.*"
2. The teacher walks into the classroom. None of the students are in their seats and
   they're all making noise. She says,
   "_____ ."
3. The teacher is very angry because one student just won't stop talking. She finally
   says, "_____ ."
4. Sue wants to go to the movies so she says to her husband Ted,
   "_____ ." Ted doesn't want to go out.

47

He replies, "_____ ."

5. A man and his dog stop in front of a store and the man leaves the dog outside by the entrance. Before going in the store, he says to the dog, "_____ ."

6. There's a loud party going on in Tom's apartment. Somebody rings the doorbell, but Tom is too far from the door to open it. He calls out, "_____ ."

7. A robber walks into a bank, draws his gun, stares intently at everyone in the bank, and says, "_____ ."

8. Mary has met some nice people and she is trying to persuade them to come and visit her some time. She says, "_____ ."

9. Mr. Wilson has had a problem with teenagers who stand outside his grocery store for hours at a time. He doesn't want any loiterers there, so he put up a sign saying, "_____ ."

10. Mrs. Stern has just arrived at the doctor's office for an appointment. The doctor is not ready for her yet, so the receptionist wants her to have a seat. She says politely, "_____ ."

Listen

A. Listen carefully to the information. Then check the box next to the statement that is true according to the information you have heard.

1. ☐ a. Arthur helped Mary move the furniture.
   ☐ b. Arthur is too weak to move furniture.
   ☐ c. Mary moved the furniture without Arthur's help.

2. ☐ a. Jean's sister couldn't go the theater.
   ☐ b. Jean couldn't go the theater.
   ☐ c. Jean didn't want to go to the theater.

3. ☐ a. John should go to the theater right now.
   ☐ b. John doesn't need to leave for the theater yet.
   ☐ c. John has missed part of the play.

4. ☐ a. Anna saw the doctor yesterday.
   ☐ b. Anna had to see the doctor yesterday.
   ☐ c. Anna had a doctor's appointment yesterday.

5. ☐ a. She said, "Somebody help me with this, please."
   ☐ b. She said, "Help!"
   ☐ c. She said, "Don't anybody help me."

6. ☐ a. Katia spoke to her friend on the phone.
   ☐ b. Katia met her friend in New York.
   ☐ c. Katia returned her friend's phone call.

B. Listen carefully to the brief dialogue, or part of a dialogue, and to the question that follows. Then check the box next to the correct answer.

1. ☐ a. Alice told it to him.
   ☐ b. Robert told it to him.
   ☐ c. John told it to himself.

2. ☐ a. Because the team was called away.
   ☐ b. Because they called off the celebration.
   ☐ c. Because the victory called for a celebration.

3. ☐ a. A doctor.
   ☐ b. A relative.
   ☐ c. A police officer.

4. ☐ a. Yesterday.
   ☐ b. Tonight.
   ☐ c. Tomorrow.

Vocabulary in Context

A. Complete the conversation using the appropriate idiom from the list below. Use contractions when possible.

have got to   be supposed to   be able to

Michelle: How soon do you think you'll _____ finish fixing my car?

Mechanic: I really don't know. The boss tells me what to do, and I _____ work on that truck first.

Michelle: Do you think I'll _____ drive my car home tonight?

Mechanic: My boss always tells me to be careful about what I tell people. I _____ not _____ make any promises to our customers. But I think so.

Michelle: Great! Could I use your phone? I _____ call my husband right away. He thinks we're going out early. I won't _____ get home in time, but at least we'll _____ go out.

49

Mechanic: I _____ not _____ let anyone use the phone, but go ahead.

Michelle: Thanks.

B. Complete the sentences using the correct form of an expression from the list below.

be called away	call up	call out
call on	call back	
call for	call off	

1. They had to _____ the game because of rain.
2. It was a long trip to the hospital but she decided to _____ her friend's mother, who was sick.
3. He stood at the window and _____ to his friend on the street below.
4. The recipe _____ equal amounts of sugar and fruit.
5. It's pleasant to _____ friends who are too far away to visit.
6. The doctor _____ in the middle of dinner because of an emergency.
7. If you get a message that someone telephoned while you were out, it's polite to _____ as soon as possible.

Read

Folk Music

A.   Music has always been an expression of our universal hopes and fears. Perhaps the oldest and purest form of this expression occurs in folk music. It is an unwritten record of the beliefs and attitudes of a culture, passed on by word of mouth. In a sophisticated culture, music is usually written down and does not have to be performed to be remembered. It may be rediscovered after its composer has died. But in a society that lacks a written history, music must be passed directly from one generation to the next.

The songs which survive are probably the people's favorites. Of course, a folk song which we hear today is not exactly the same as the one our ancestors heard. It has changed through interpretations of successive generations.

Each culture develops its own songs which tell tales of heroic leaders, glorious battles, and love. One culture may adopt and change songs from another culture.

For example, a tune may appear as a ballad in German or a Christmas carol in Poland. It is unlikely that the same tune developed independently in each country. Rather, the people in a border region probably taught it to their friends nearby. Or perhaps it was transferred from area to area by a wandering minstrel, as was common during the Middle Ages. If the people in another country like the melody of a song but not the theme, they will often adopt the tune and replace the original words or story with something more suitable.

Check the box next to the correct answer.

1. Folk songs have been preserved mainly through _____ .
   ☐ a. phonograph records
   ☐ b. memory
   ☐ c. writing

2. The songs which are passed from generation to generation are
   _____ .
   ☐ a. the ones people prefer
   ☐ b. the ones with new interpretations
   ☐ c. the ones that have not changed

3. The same song often exists in many countries because _____ .
   ☐ a. each culture develops its own songs about heroic leaders, glorious battles, and love
   ☐ b. it was transferred by minstrels and people living in border regions
   ☐ c. it developed independently in each place

4. People of one country often change the words of a song because
_____ .

- [ ] a. they don't like the tune
- [ ] b. the original words are suitable
- [ ] c. they like the melody but not the theme

B.   Dance music is one of the most common forms of folk music. The oldest dances developed as part of the rituals all cultures once practiced. These included dances to celebrate birth, marriage, and death, and dances to accompany the planting and harvesting of crops. Many of these dances have disappeared with the rise of modern civilization, which is centered around cities and industrial development rather than rural areas and agriculture. Still, dancing remains popular throughout the world, and the dances of different nations are similar in many ways. For example, sword dances are performed in Scotland, England, Central Europe, and India. In some countries these probably developed independently; in other countries such as Scotland and England, they are probably an example of cultural transfer.

Although music students often argue about the original source of a particular folk song, this information is usually unknown. It is agreed, however, that a song is usually the product of one individual who is able to express his people's attitudes and feelings through music. Occasionally, a style of music may develop through group efforts. In some African societies, for example, antiphony, or alternation between groups, each singing one phrase at a time, resulted in the development of a distinct musical style.

The fact that people of all countries love to sing and dance is an example of the similarities among different cultures.

Check the box next to the correct answer.

1. Dance music was first developed _____ .
- [ ] a. in cultures centered in cities
- [ ] b. for use with rituals
- [ ] c. with the rise of modern civilization

2. The fact that sword dancing occurs in a number of different countries is
_____ .

- [ ] a. basically a result of cultural transfer
- [ ] b. always a result of independent development
- [ ] c. a result of both independent development and cultural transfer

52

3. Music students believe that most folk songs are created by

_____ .

☐ a. one person
☐ b. groups of people
☐ c. several villages

4. Antiphony is an example of folk music created by _____ .

☐ a. a talented individual
☐ b. music students
☐ c. a group of people

Composition

A. **A good paragraph must have unity. To achieve this unity, the writer should treat only one idea in each paragraph. The main idea is expressed in the topic sentence and is supported by other more specific statements. The following text has two main ideas; it should, therefore, be broken up into two paragraphs. Underline the two main ideas and circle the word that should begin each of the two paragraphs.**

Centuries ago, the Bermuda Islands were known as the "Isles of Devils." Remote, uninhabited, and surrounded by dangerous reefs lying just beneath the surface of the turquoise sea, Bermuda was a navigational menace. Mariners who sailed the trade routes of the Atlantic treated the islands with the same fearsome respect as the plague. There are about 150 small islands which make up Bermuda. The seven largest of them are connected by bridges and causeways. Since the islands are close together, they are called the "Island of Bermuda," as if they were just one island.

B. **Write a short, unified paragraph explaining why you liked a movie, TV show, or play you have seen recently. First, identify the movie, show, or play by writing a topic sentence similar to the one below. Then, in several supporting sentences, tell what you liked about it. Finally, give your general evaluation of it in a concluding sentence.**

Topic sentence: One (movie) I have enjoyed recently is (*Star Wars*).

_____

_____

_____

_____

_____

_____

_____

_____

_____

Word Game

Put the two words together to make a new word. The two words will form either a single word, a hyphenated word, or a two-word expression. In some cases, the word in one column can combine with more than one word from the other column. Write the word(s) in the blanks.

1.	drive	_____	shell
2.	shopping	_____	agent
3.	get	_____	way
4.	watch	_____	maker
5.	space	_____	center
6.	egg	_____	craft
7.	business	_____	trip
8.	reservation	_____	together
9.	area	_____	release
10.	public	_____	relations
11.	ticket	_____	code
12.	press	_____	clerk

Unit 3

Complete

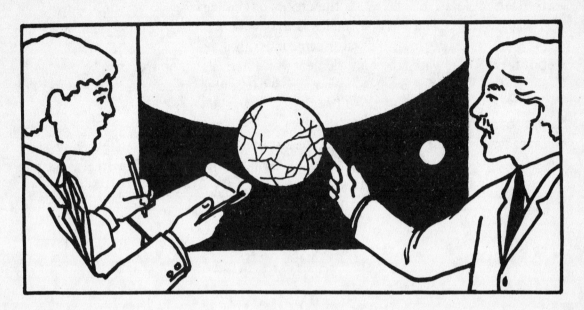

A reporter is _____ a scientist for the United States _____ Agency concerning _____ made by the Voyager 2 spacecraft.

Reporter: What's the _____ important information you've _____ from the Voyager 2 mission?

Scientist: _____ now believe it's possible _____ some form of life _____ on Europa, which is one of Jupiter's _____ .

Reporter: _____ evidence is there of _____on Europa?

Scientist: Europa _____ to have water, and water is the _____ requirement for life _____ we know it.

Reporter: Is water the _____ similarity between Earth and Europa?

Scientist: Yes. We believe that _____ and Europa evolved in the _____ way, but _____ Jupiter dimmed, Europa's development _____ . Jupiter was Europa's _____ source.

Reporter: What does _____ surface of Europa look _____ ?

Scientist: _____ our pictures, it looks like a _____ eggshell that has _____ cracked.

Reporter: Can you _____ water on Europa's surface?

Scientist: No, but we're fairly _____ that the surface is a crust of _____ about five miles _____ . The ice covers a global _____ perhaps 60 miles _____ .

Reporter: _____ can you be sure there's _____ on Europa?

Scientist: We _____ the cracks on the surface. As a _____ , we've learned that the ice is thin _____ to break, and when that _____ water can come through.

Reporter: ____ water the only element you _____ on Europa?

Scientist: No. When the _____ breaks, what comes up isn't _____ water. But we haven't identified the _____ elements.

Reporter: Do you know _____ the ice _____ cracked?

Scientist: No. But NASA _____ be launching the Galileo satellite into orbit _____ Jupiter in _____ mid-1980's and we'll learn _____ about Europa then.

Write

A. Complete the following sentences with an appropriate cause, purpose, or consequence.

1. Many people give up eating desserts so that *(they won't gain weight)*.
2. Since smoking is dangerous for your health, _____
   _____ .
3. Divorce is increasing in many countries because _____
   _____ .
4. Many people would rather live in the country than in the city because _____
   _____ .
5. I'm saving up a little money so that _____
   _____ .
6. So that I won't lose my keys, _____
   _____ .
7. My parents got very angry with me once because _____
   _____ .
8. Since the weather is so bad today, _____

   _____ .

B. Write a reasonable consequence for each of the situations below, using the expression in parentheses.

1. We were hungry and hadn't eaten all day.   (so)
   (So we went to a coffee shop and had sandwiches.)
2. Few of the students had studied for the exam.   (consequently)
   _____.
3. Gasoline prices keep going up, and it has become very expensive to run big cars.   (as a result)
   _____.
4. Elaine forgot to set her alarm before she went to bed.   (because of this)
   _____.
5. My best friend hasn't written or called in five months.   (therefore)
   _____.
6. Alicia went out in the rain without a raincoat or an umbrella.   (as a result)
   _____.
7. My paycheck never seems to cover all my bills.   (Thus)
   _____.
8. Alfred got caught in a traffic jam on his way to the airport.   (for this reason)
   _____.

C. Rewrite these sentences in the passive. Do not include a <u>by</u> phrase unless it is essential to the meaning of the sentence.

1. You should keep meat in the refrigerator.
   Meat should be kept in the refrigerator.
2. Earthquakes have killed hundreds of people in the last few years.
   Hundreds of people have been killed by earthquakes in the last few years.
3. People commit many crimes in large cities.
   _____.
4. The police catch very few criminals, however.
   _____.
5. Because of the gasoline shortage, people in the U.S. are buying fewer large cars.
   _____.
6. Car companies are making small cars these days.
   _____.
7. You shouldn't throw away furniture and other household items.
   _____.
8. You can give these items to various charity organizations.
   _____.

9. They're showing an excellent film at the Regency Theater.

_____ .

10. I went there last night, but they had already sold all the tickets before I arrived.

_____ .

D. Rewrite these sentences changing the verbs in italics to the passive with <u>get</u>. Include a phrase with <u>by</u> only when it is indicated in parentheses.

1. I hope they *catch* the thief.
   I hope the thief gets caught.
2. Robert's father *punished* him for bringing a snake into the house.   (by his father)
   Robert got punished by his father for bringing a snake into the house.
3. A car *hit* Philip the other day as he was crossing the street.   (by a car)

_____ .

4. The boss will *fire* Beth if she doesn't start coming to work on time.

_____ .

5. Tom is very sensitive and Jane often *hurts* his feelings.   (by Jane)

_____ .

6. I *burned* the towel because I left it near the stove and it caught fire.

_____ .

7. Someone is always *breaking* the record player.   (by someone)

_____ .

8. We don't *clean* our house often enough.

_____ .

9. They're going to *promote* Tim very soon because he's doing an excellent job.

_____ .

10. Someone *left* the blanket out in the rain, and the rain *ruined* it.

_____ .

Listen

A. Listen carefully to the information. Then check the box next to the statement that is true according to the information you have heard.

1. ☐ a. The government is trying to conserve energy.
   ☐ b. The government wants us to use as much energy as we can.
   ☐ c. The government is worried that thermostats will be wasted.

2. ☐ a. Water shouldn't be wasted.
   ☐ b. Water shouldn't be saved.
   ☐ c. Water shouldn't be used.

3. ☐ a. We're going on a picnic so that we can pack a lunch.
   ☐ b. Because we're going on a picnic, we'll need to pack a lunch.
   ☐ c. Since we need to pack a lunch, we're going on a picnic.

4. ☐ a. The rescue team doesn't know about the accident.
   ☐ b. The rescue team will save the man.
   ☐ c. The rescue team cannot save the man.

5. ☐ a. I ought to look for another job.
   ☐ b. I'll leave the company soon.
   ☐ c. I'll have a more important position.

B. Listen carefully to the brief dialogue, or part of a dialogue, and to the question that follows. Then check the box next to the correct answer.

1. ☐ a. Once a year.
   ☐ b. Five times a year.
   ☐ c. Once every five years.

2. ☐ a. That the first speaker go to the movies before Jan's party.
   ☐ b. That the first speaker go to the movies after Jan's party.
   ☐ c. That the first speaker go only to Jan's party.

3. ☐ a. The poor person.
   ☐ b. The son.
   ☐ c. The mother.

4. ☐ a. Under the water.
   ☐ b. On the surface.
   ☐ c. Under the crust.

Vocabulary in Context

A. Complete the conversation using the appropriate idiom from the list below.

how about   what about   how come   what if

Sharon: Larry, _____ going to a movie tonight?

Larry: I've been tired all day, Sharon. _____ tomorrow night instead?

Sharon: _____ you're always so tired? Every time I want to go out, you'd rather stay home.

Larry: I really want to go out, but I'm exhausted. _____ I promise that we'll go out tomorrow instead? Would that be O.K.?

Sharon: Sure. That sounds good. It's a date.

B. Complete the sentences using the correct form of an expression from the list below.

give away   give in   give out
give back   give up   give off

1. The flowers outside their window _____ a perfume that filled their room each evening.
2. When you borrow something, try to _____ it _____ promptly.
3. I like to _____ anything I haven't used or worn for two years.
4. She knew that the fight was lost, so she decided to _____ .
5. When Peter realized that his own plan wouldn't work, he knew that he'd have to _____ to his boss's suggestion.
6. Joanne stayed in the bicycle race until her energy _____ .

Read

Elise rolls merrily along on a bike—at 60

A.   In her 60 years, former circus performer Elise Briskey has swallowed swords, eaten fire, and twirled snakes. But that's all kid stuff, compared with the 1,000-mile bike ride she just completed between her hometown of Tampa, Fla., and New York City, reports Joyce White of the Daily News.

"I just wanted to prove that somebody my age could do it," Briskey said yesterday. She admitted that her feet and legs ached. "I saw my doctor before I left Tampa. He told me that with my heart condition, he wasn't going to guarantee that I would make it. But when he saw that I was determined, he didn't try to hold me back."

Elise set out from Tampa on May 20, her 10-speed Raleigh touring bike equipped with just about everything she needs. Attached to the rear is a two-wheel cart. It carries her suitcase, packed with eight changes of clothing; maps, a box lunch (just in case there isn't a restaurant on her route) and a medicine kit stocked with the nitroglycerin tablets she takes for a mild angina condition. She also has other medication for her diabetes.

"I'm not torturing my body," Briskey insisted, shrugging aside all notions that she might be carrying her physical fitness feats a bit too far. "Of course, I get mild leg cramps from time to time. My shoulder and arms ache a bit, and I do get tired. But it's a pleasant tiredness. No different than how you feel after a busy day at work."

Check the box next to the correct answer.

1. Elise Briskey's doctor told her that _____ .
   ☐ a. she shouldn't take the trip.
   ☐ b. she might not reach New York City
   ☐ c. the trip would cause her heart trouble

2. In her suitcase Elise carries _____ .
   ☐ a. extra clothes
   ☐ b. lunch
   ☐ c. medicine

3. The worst effect of the trip so far has been _____ .
- [ ] a. aches and cramps
- [ ] b. mild angina
- [ ] c. diabetes

B. A cyclist for more than 35 years, Briskey's first long-distance trip—from Coney Island to Tampa—was in 1966. Since then, she has refined her pedaling to a polished routine that carries her between 40 and 60 miles per day.

Her day begins at 5 or 6 A.M. with a hearty breakfast of eggs, toast, coffee, and perhaps sausage or ham. She bikes steadily for the next four hours, then stops for lunch and an hour's rest. Back in the seat, Briskey pedals for another two or three hours, then rests for another hour. She bikes another two hours, repeats her hour of rest, pedals for two more hours, and then searches for a place to rest her weary body for the night.

"I never make hotel reservations because I can never be sure when I will arrive in a town," she said. "So I just get to a city and if I'm not too tired, I try to look around for a cheap hotel. Sometimes I end up paying more than I had planned, but I don't worry about it because the most important thing is a place to sleep."

After a few days' rest here, she'll pedal up to Maine. Then, it's off to Chicago, where she plans to spend the winter. Next spring, it'll be "Westward Ho" to Washington, Oregon, California, New Mexico and Oklahoma. "That trip may last three years," she mused. "Before it's over, I probably will have covered all 48 states on the mainland."

Going like 60: That's Elise Briskey.

Check the box next to the correct answer.

1. Briskey has been a long-distance cyclist _____ .
- [ ] a. for over 60 years
- [ ] b. for over 35 years
- [ ] c. since 1966

2. Briskey cycles _____ every day.
- [ ] a. 5 to 6 hours
- [ ] b. as much as 11 hours
- [ ] c. around 8 hours

3. After she finishes her present trip, Briskey plans to _____ .
- [ ] a. take a long vacation
- [ ] b. spend three more years traveling
- [ ] c. cycle back to Tampa

Composition

A. Newspaper articles can be constructed in many different ways, but the most typical articles generally begin with a paragraph which answers the questions <u>who</u>, <u>what</u>, <u>where</u>, and <u>when</u>. The paragraphs are usually very short so that people can read the article very quickly. Notice that in the article below the first paragraph gives a summary of the main facts. The second two paragraphs give supporting, explanatory details.

Bridgeport, May 1—Two Bridgeport residents called the police early this morning to report what they believed was a prowler lurking close to their homes.

Alice Bodin, the first of the callers, said she had been awakened around 3:00 A.M. by a noise coming from behind the garage, which is located near her bedroom window. John Strand called fifteen minutes later to report that he had been awakened by the screams of his son, who thought he had heard someone attempting to enter the back door of the house. Strand lives next door to the Bodin residence.

A police investigation showed that the large garbage containers at both homes had been overturned, and that several other homes on the small street had been similarly attacked. Police speculated that raccoons from the nearby woods may have come to the neighborhood looking for food.

B. Find a news item that interests you and write it up as a short news article following the format above. The first paragraph should include answers to the following questions: What happened? Who was involved? Where did it happen? When did it happen? The second and third paragraphs should present supporting details.

Word Game

Read each sentence, and then find a synonym for the word in italics from the list of words below on the right.

1. The man has good manners. He is very *courteous*.
2. Stop making up *alibis*; you simply must learn to arrive on time.
3. Their *dispute* over politics made it impossible for them to be friends.

4. The true meaning of the speaker's words were *misconstrued* by the audience.
5. Because of the workers' *proficiency*, they were given a promotion.
6. His remarks were considered *insulting* by the teacher, so he was asked to leave the class.
7. That child always has an *alert* expression on her face. It is no surprise that she scored highest on the exam.
8. A dinner party is no place for a *monologue*; stop talking so much.

1. courteous	_____	soliloquy
2. alibi	_____	polite
3. dispute	_____	excuse
4. misconstrue	_____	argument
5. proficiency	_____	misinterpret
6. insulting	_____	attentive
7. alert	_____	skill
8. monologue	_____	offensive

Unit 4

Complete

Dolores Andersson is _____ a plane reservation to take a _____ trip to Washington, D.C., _____ she has to meet with some _____ .

Dolores: *(Dials 657-2300 and listens)*

Agent: Reservation desk, Transcontinental Airlines. _____ I help you?

Dolores: I'd _____ to make reservations for a _____ to Washington, D.C. on the _____ of March 10th.

Agent: _____ the 11 o'clock flight be _____ right?

Dolores: Yes, that's O.K.

Agent: Will you ____ flying first class or _____ ?

Dolores: Coach.

Agent: And when will you be _____ ?

Dolores: ____ March 15th. _____ like an afternoon _____ , if possible.

Agent: There's a flight ____ 3:16.

Dolores: That'll ____ fine.

Agent: Thank you. Your name, _____ ?

Dolores: Dolores—D-o-l-o-r-e-s—Andersson, _____ two *s*'s.

Agent: Will you _____ up your ticket or ____ you want us to _____ it to you?

Dolores: I'll pick ____ up. How much _____ it be?

Agent: _____ trip will be two hundred and thirty-six dollars. _____ we have your _____ number, please?

Dolores: 248-3129.

Agent: And the area _____ , please?

Dolores: 312.

Agent: Thank _____ . You have confirmed _____ for March 10 on Transcontinental flight No. 241 _____ Chicago at 11 A.M. and arriving _____ Washington at 1:55 _____ . You are also confirmed on _____ flight 242 leaving Washington _____ March 15th _____ 3:15 P.M. and arriving _____ Chicago at 4:15 P.M.

_____ the airport in Washington, Dolores claims her _____ in the baggage area and asks a _____ for information.

Dolores: Excuse me, sir. How can I _____ to the Grand Hotel?

Skycap: You can _____ a taxi, a limousine, or the Metro, _____ .

Dolores: Which is _____ fastest?

Skycap: The taxi, ma'am. But it _____ more.

Dolores: Where can I _____ a taxi?

Skycap: _____ over there.

Write

A. Fill in the blanks with the correct pronouns. Choose from I, me, he, him, and we. Most of the pronouns are used more than once.

I was waiting for a taxi in the rain when a car pulled up. I heard a voice ask *me* where _____ was going. At first _____ didn't recognize the voice, but then _____ realized it was my friend Felix.

_____ replied that _____ was going to a meeting downtown, and asked _____ if he could take _____ . Felix told _____ that _____ could and _____ soon were on our way.

Felix said that _____ hadn't seen _____ for a long time. I told _____ that _____ had been very busy. _____ asked _____ if _____ would like to have dinner with _____ the next night, but I had to refuse.

I told _____ that _____ would call _____ some time, but then _____ never did.

B. Read the following account of a conversation between Martin and Florence. Then write it in dialogue form.

Martin asked Florence if she liked to dance. She said that she didn't know how to dance very well. Martin said that he would teach her. Florence replied that it wouldn't be easy. Martin asked her if she had a record player. Florence said yes but that it was old. Martin said that he would come over Tuesday night. Florence asked him what kind of music they needed. Martin replied that they needed disco music. Florence said that she had a lot of disco music.

Martin: _____
Florence: _____
Martin: _____
Florence: _____
Martin: _____
Florence: _____
Martin: _____
Florence: _____
Martin: _____
Florence: _____

C. Write sentences expressing a wish about the underlined phrase. Be sure to use the correct verb tense.

1. I can't have that job because <u>I don't speak Chinese</u>.
   I wish I spoke Chinese.
2. It's raining very hard, and <u>I forgot my umbrella</u>!
   I wish I hadn't forgotten my umbrella.
3. <u>I went to see that movie</u> and I thought it was a waste of time.
   _____.
4. <u>I don't know how to swim</u>, so I can't go on that boating trip.
   _____.
5. I hate to go to parties because <u>I'm not a good conversationalist</u>.
   _____.
6. <u>I can't go away this weekend</u> because my relatives are coming to visit.
   _____.
7. <u>I wasn't able to keep the dog</u> because I moved to a studio apartment.
   _____.
8. My parents and I had a big argument and now <u>they won't talk to me</u>.
   _____.

Listen

A. **Listen carefully to the information. Then check the box next to the statement that is true according to the information you have heard.**

1. ☐ a. William has just left Chicago.
   ☐ b. William will be flying to Chicago in the morning.
   ☐ c. William has reservations for a flight to San Francisco.

2. ☐ a. The woman said, "Do you need any help?"
   ☐ b. The woman said, "I need some help."
   ☐ c. The woman said, "Somebody help me, please."

3. ☐ a. Jane thinks she'll travel all over the world.
   ☐ b. Jane would like to travel all over the world.
   ☐ c. Jane travels all over the world.

4. ☐ a. The project might be two days late.
   ☐ b. The project will be two days late.
   ☐ c. The project is already two days late.

5. ☐ a. The children went to the park.
   ☐ b. The children and their teacher went to the park.
   ☐ c. The children and a parent went to the park.

B. **Listen carefully to the brief dialogue, or part of a dialogue, and to the question that follows. Then check the box next to the correct answer.**

1. ☐ a. More than he wanted to.
   ☐ b. Less than he expected to.
   ☐ c. Just what he expected to.

2. ☐ a. "I'm sorry."
   ☐ b. "Please."
   ☐ c. "As a matter of fact."

3. ☐ a. "By the way . . ."
   ☐ b. "In any case . . ."
   ☐ c. "As a matter of fact . . ."

4. ☐ a. That he might send flowers.
   ☐ b. That he would send flowers.
   ☐ c. That he could visit Mr. Hunter.

Vocabulary in Context

A. Complete the sentences using the appropriate idiom from the list below.

as a matter of fact   by the way   in any case

Joan: Are you coming to the conference tomorrow?

Paul: Yes, I am. _____ Joan, are you going to attend that board meeting tonight?

Joan: Yes, _____ , I am. Why do you ask?

Paul: I don't want to miss anything, but I may have to leave early.

Joan: Don't worry. I'll tell you all about it and, _____ , you can always look at my notes of the meeting.

Paul: _____ I was hoping you'd say that! Thanks!

B. Complete the sentences using the correct form of an expression from the list below.

go along with   go back   go down   go on with
go away   go by   go into   go up

1. Last summer my parents hoped to _____ for two weeks, but they had too much work to do at home.
2. If my parents took a summer vacation each year, they would always _____ to the same place.
3. We decided that we'd rather _____ the group than go by ourselves.
4. The police officer told him that there had been an accident, but she didn't want to _____ detail about it on the phone.
5. They wanted him to _____ the story so that they could hear how it ended.
6. The price of gasoline continues to _____ .
7. I love to sit in a city park and watch all the people _____ .
8. When the temperature _____ , everyone dresses warmly and moves quickly.

Read

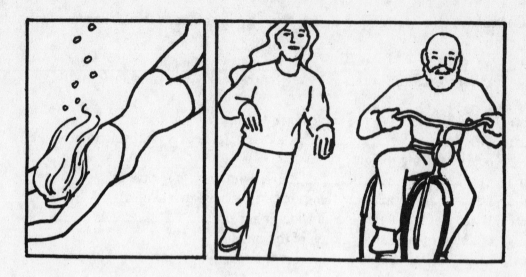

Building Physical Stamina

A.   Everyone should be concerned about physical fitness—everyone, that is, who wants to live a long, active life. Fitness doesn't mean pure physical strength, the kind needed to lift weights, for example; it means overall good health. Physically fit people are free from disease, and have muscles and joints in good working order. But more important, they have "physical stamina," the ability to be active for long periods of time without great fatigue. Stamina depends on strong cardiovascular (heart and vessel) and pulmonary (lung) systems. Fortunately, it is the aspect of physical fitness over which we have the most control. A person can develop it simply through regular exercise.

An understanding of physical stamina depends on a knowledge of body activity. Every movement of the body requires energy. Energy comes from burning fuel—the food we eat—by means of the oxygen we breathe in. Food is stored in the body and used as needed, but oxygen cannot be stored. It must be continuously supplied by breathing. During normal activity, oxygen demands are easily met. But activities such as running, swimming, and prolonged walking demand more oxygen than the lungs can supply with regular breathing. We have all experienced what happens when the body is trying to make up for an oxygen deficit. The chest moves in and out rapidly as the lungs struggle to take in more air. The heart beats fast in order to speed blood (which carries the oxygen) to all parts of the body. The end result is fatigue.

The level of exertion that brings on fatigue is an accurate measure of a person's physical stamina. Almost everyone can perform normal activities without fatigue, but unfit people can become fatigued simply by taking a short walk or climbing a flight of stairs. Their lungs aren't strong enough to take in the necessary oxygen, and their hearts aren't strong enough to pump the oxygen to all parts of the body. Fit people, on the other hand, can withstand a higher level of exertion over a longer period of time.

Check the box next to the correct answer.

1. A person with stamina always _____ .
   - ☐ a. lifts weights
   - ☐ b. has a strong heart and strong lungs
   - ☐ c. is free from disease

2. Energy for body activity comes from _____ .
   - ☐ a. strong muscles
   - ☐ b. regular exercise
   - ☐ c. food and oxygen

3. An oxygen deficit is caused by _____ .
   - ☐ a. the heart beating too fast
   - ☐ b. activities requiring extra energy
   - ☐ c. strong lungs

4. People without physical stamina can't _____ .
   - ☐ a. perform normal activities without fatigue
   - ☐ b. withstand long periods of exertion
   - ☐ c. measure fatigue accurately

B. The best way to conquer fatigue is to build physical stamina by strengthening the heart and lungs; and it is one of the miracles of human physiology that this can be done in a matter of months with proper exercise. The best kind of exercise is "aerobics," or exercise requiring large amounts of air. Running, swimming, cycling, and long-distance walking all provide aerobic exercise. They demand much more oxygen than normal, but not so much that the activity cannot be maintained for long periods of time. If these activities are practiced regularly with gradual increases in effort, the heart and lungs can reach optimal strength.

Dr. Kenneth Cooper, in his book *Aerobics,* has developed a system by which a person can slowly build stamina. A person accumulates points each week based on the kind of exercise performed and the time spent doing it. The average person can earn enough points to be considered in top physical condition by walking three miles a day in less than forty-five minutes, five times a week; or by swimming a half a mile in about twenty minutes, four times a week.

Aerobic exercise can be free, convenient, and enjoyable. It releases emotional pressures and adds variety to daily activities. As for the need to strengthen the heart and lungs, statistics show the unfortunate results of a lack of exercise. A high number of deaths from heart failure in forty- to sixty-year-olds occur when an activity such as mowing the lawn or shoveling snow puts a sudden strain on the body. It seems that in the long run, the investment of two or three hours a week is well worth the return of added years of living in sound health.

Check the box next to the correct answer.

1. Aerobic excercises build the heart and lungs because they
_____ .
- [ ] a. require a lot of oxygen
- [ ] b. can't be maintained for long periods of time
- [ ] c. require great effort

2. Dr. Cooper has developed _____ .
- [ ] a. a system for building stamina
- [ ] b. special exercises for stamina
- [ ] c. a system of building muscles

3. Aerobic exercises are good for _____ .
- [ ] a. straining the body
- [ ] b. releasing emotional pressure
- [ ] c. heart failure

4. If people do not exercise they will _____ .
- [ ] a. have few health problems
- [ ] b. be in top physical condition
- [ ] c. shorten their lives

Composition

A. Write a paragraph telling about the picture sequence below. Use the past tense throughout and indirect speech whenever appropriate.

A woman came into the waiting room of a doctor's office. _____
_____
_____
_____
_____
_____
_____
_____
_____

B. Tell about an amusing or irritating encounter you have had with a stranger in a store or on the street. Use the past tense throughout, and use indirect speech to retell your conversation with this person.

Word Game

Have a race with your classmates to see who can figure out the eight scrambled words below. All of them are from this unit.

1. tinsaot _____
2. gsengitehis _____
3. rotsitu _____
4. sepgraens ___-_____

5. oatprntonsarit _____
6. ietvsanrero _____
7. wsyuab _____
8. enntcocino _____

Unit 5

Complete

Anton Souza __has__ been planning to __buy__ a small radio for a __long__ time. Until yesterday when he __went__ shopping with a friend, he had __been__ hoping to find a __good__ one at a reasonable __price__ . This was his __experience__ inside a store that sells _____ goods and small appliances.

Clerk: May I __help__ you?

Anton: __I'd__ like to buy a small _____ .

Clerk: AM and _____ ?

Anton: _____ , I want to hear _____ from abroad.

Clerk: Then you _____ would want a short-wave _____ .

Anton: Yes, _____ I want to hear _____ programs, too.

Clerk: O.K. We _____ this portable radio with all _____ bands. You can listen to stations all _____ the world.

Anton: It's nice. _____ you put it on _____ wave so I can hear _____ ?

Clerk: _____ . But you _____ get good short-_____ reception inside the store _____ the day.

Anton: How _____ does it cost?

Clerk: This is _____ sale. _____ month it's fifty dollars _____ the regular price. It was three ninety-nine. _____ you can buy it _____ three forty-nine.

75

Friend: That's _____ than you wanted to _____ , isn't it? I thought you _____ a small radio.

Anton: I _____ you're right. Do you have _____ smaller, and . . . _____ expensive?

Clerk: We have this _____ radio. You can use it _____ as an alarm clock and a radio.

Anton: But it doesn't have _____ wave. I want something _____ short wave.

Friend: And you don't _____ the clock.

Anton: That's right. _____ you have a small short-wave _____ ?

Clerk: Yes. We have _____ one. Good quality. _____ bands. Guaranteed _____ a year. The _____ is forty-nine fifty.

Anton: That's just about _____ I had in _____ . Can I hear it?

Clerk: Sure. Let's _____ it in. There. This _____ is for tone.

Anton: Hmmm. Good. Does it _____ on batteries?

Clerk: Yes. It has four small _____ .

Anton: Are they _____ in the price?

Clerk: No. They're seventy-five cents _____ .

Anton: I think I'd _____ check the prices in a _____ other stores first, and ____ I decide to buy _____ one, I'll be _____ tomorrow. Thanks _____ much for your _____ .

Write

A. Using the cues, write sentences with the present perfect progressive and <u>for</u> or <u>since</u>.

1. Patrick/pay taxes/1976.
   Patrick has been paying taxes since 1976.
2. the campers/hike/ten days.

   _____ .
3. Maria/study bookkeeping/last month.

   _____ .
4. Tom/sew his own clothes/twelve years.

   _____ .
5. Anne/study yoga/she returned from India.

   _____ .
6. the water/boil/twenty minutes.

   _____ .

7. Mr. and Mrs. Shell/rest/lunch.

_____.

8. Harry/lose sleep over his job/weeks.

_____.

B. Rewrite the sentences using the past perfect progressive and the connector _when_ as in the examples.

1. Mr. Olsen was planning to go to Indonesia, and then his company asked him to go to Brazil.
   Mr. Olsen had been planning to go to Indonesia when his company asked him to go to Brazil.
2. The fire burned for hours, and then the fire fighters arrived.
   The fire had been burning for hours when the fire fighters arrived.
3. The dog barked for a long time, and then his owner fed him.

_____.

4. We sat in the restaurant for an hour, and then our lunch was finally served.

_____.

5. Lester sold ties for years, and then they made him manager.

_____.

6. Bob was shopping for a shirt, but then he saw a beautiful tie.

_____.

7. Catherine drank tea for years, but then her doctor told her to stop.

_____.

8. Michiko worked as a model for months, but then she got a part in a movie.

_____.

C. Fill in the tag questions and short answers in the following excerpt from the TV program "Guess My Occupation."

Panelist: You work outdoors, _____ ?
  Guest: In a way.
Panelist: If it were sunny while you were working, you would get burned,
_____ ?
  Guest: No, _____ .
Panelist: Hmmm. You use special equipment in your work, _____ ?
  Guest: Yes, _____ .
Panelist: You need special training for your work, _____ ?
  Guest: Yes, _____ .
Panelist: Your work is dangerous, _____ ?

Guest: Sometimes.

Panelist: You're an astronaut, _____ ?

Guest: No, _____ .

Panelist: I've seen your picture in the newspapers, _____ ?

Guest: No, _____ .

Panelist: We give up.

Guest: I fooled you, _____ . I'm a deep sea diver.

Listen

A. Listen carefully to the information. Then check the box next to the statement that is true according to the information you have heard.

1. ☐ a. Christopher is a teacher, but not a coach.
   ☐ b. Christopher is a coach, but not a teacher.
   ☐ c. Christopher is both a teacher and a coach.

2. ☐ a. Helen was listening at the door.
   ☐ b. Helen is still listening at the door.
   ☐ c. Helen will listen at the door.

3. ☐ a. He was fired before he could quit.
   ☐ b. He quit before he could be fired.
   ☐ c. He was fired because he had been planning to quit.

4. ☐ a. Henry is working in the garden.
   ☐ b. Henry was working in the garden.
   ☐ c. Henry will be working in the garden.

5. ☐ a. The bride and groom had been married for three months.
   ☐ b. The bride and groom had to wait three more months.
   ☐ c. The couple had been together for three months.

B. Listen carefully to the brief dialogue, or part of a dialogue, and to the question that follows. Then check the box next to the correct answer.

1. ☐ a. The store manager. 2. ☐ a. A friendly one.
   ☐ b. A customer.   ☐ b. A pleasant one.
   ☐ c. A tape recording.   ☐ c. A difficult one.

3. □ a. To take the blue one.
   □ b. To take the red one.
   □ c. To take the blue one and the red one.

4. □ a. An excellent writer.
   □ b. An average writer.
   □ c. A fast writer.

Vocabulary in Context

A. Complete the conversation using the appropriate idiom from the list below.

    just the same   on second thought   to tell you the truth

Charlotte: Where are you going on vacation this summer?
George: _____ , I haven't really given it much thought. Maybe I'll go to California. . . . _____ , I don't think I can afford to go anywhere.
Charlotte: Everyone needs a vacation.
George: _____ , if I worry about money the whole time, it won't be a vacation anyway.

B. Complete the sentences using the correct form of an expression from the list below.

    put on   put out   put away
    put up with   put off   put down

1. It's not good to _____ a job that has to be done.
2. The first warm day of spring they _____ all their winter clothing.
3. He could hardly wait to _____ his new summer suit.
4. Her parents told her to _____ her fork while she was talking.
5. The teacher wouldn't _____ bad behavior.
6. Many fires could be avoided if people carefully _____ their cigarettes.

Read

Advertising Then and Now

A. Advertising is the tool that has always been used to convince the public to buy products. In the beginning, it was a basic and crude tool. Craftsmen cried out to passersby, telling the virtues of their wares. As time passed, advertising became more refined and sophisticated. Today, newspapers, magazines, radio, and television use a variety of means to introduce the public to the many products developed through technology.

Advertising probably began when people started producing a surplus of goods which they could offer to one another. In ancient times, advertising was done orally. Public criers announced information about articles for sale along with news of current events.

The Romans started using recorded advertisements. They smoothed and whitened areas on a wall where advertisements could be written or carved, and sculptors lettered and illustrated stone or terra cotta tablets advertising various goods and services.

In the Middle Ages, people continued to use verbal announcements and written messages, but a new form of advertising, using symbols, was developed as well. Shops displayed a special symbol to indicate what goods or services could be found inside. The striped barber's pole, for example, advertised that the man in the shop would shave your beard, cut your hair, pull your teeth, and perform minor surgery.

The Industrial Revolution caused an explosion in the advertising field. The abundance of luxury goods, coming both from new inventions and from trade with different parts of the world, meant that consumers had to be told more about products than ever before. They had to be persuaded that they needed all these new products and that one product was superior to its many competitors. In addition, new inventions made it possible to duplicate advertisements in quantity. The buying public was soon being exposed to endless amounts of advertising.

Check the box next to the correct answer.

1. The earliest advertising was done by _____ .
   - ☐ a. passersby
   - ☐ b. public criers
   - ☐ c. recorded messages

2. The first written advertisements appeared _____ .
   ☐ a. in Roman times
   ☐ b. in the Middle Ages
   ☐ c. during the Industrial Revolution

3. The striped barber's pole is an example of _____ advertising.
   ☐ a. oral
   ☐ b. symbolic
   ☐ c. written

4. There was an abundance of consumer goods after the Industrial Revolution because _____ .
   ☐ a. new inventions created new products
   ☐ b. advertisements were produced in quantity
   ☐ c. the public need persuasion

B.　　Advertising soon became a professional business, the job of specialists who pooled their efforts in advertising agencies. Agencies analyzed the market for a product, selected the proper media (newspapers, magazines, etc.) in which to advertise, and wrote and designed advertisements. They began to get involved not only in the creation of advertising, but also in the creation of new products, new markets, and even new consumer needs.

In the 1920s, scientific developments had a great influence on the field. Advertisers stopped believing that products would sell themselves and started to back their efforts with scientific methods instead. Agencies conducted both market and consumer research. They systematically investigated all the factors in selling: the aspects of the product, the character and mood of prospective buyers, the buyers' geographic location, and the buyers' purchasing power.

Since that time, advertising has attracted a lot of criticism because of two questionable techniques. First, advertisers often exaggerate the virtues of a product. Products only too often are not what they are advertised to be. Second, advertisers often try to create a need for a product in the minds of consumers when no need exists in reality.

Despite these criticisms, advertising continues to catch the eye of the consumer, who continues to buy. Motivational research seeks to explain why people buy the things they do. Researchers have observed that in a "buying situation," people often act emotionally and impulsively. They react subconsciously to the images and designs on the packaging of a product. Their subconscious directs their actions in a number of ways. For example, they may be willing to pay up to $4.00 or more for a facial cream, but not more than $.75 for a bar of soap. They buy under the illusion that the facial cream will improve their appearance while the soap will simply make them clean. Modern advertisers realize that their task is to find images which have an emotional appeal for consumers.

Advertising has come a long way since the stone carvings in ancient Rome, but the basic point—to sell a product—remains the same. The nature of the products and the philosophy of advertising have changed, however. Ancient advertising tried simply to give information about those products that were necessities of life. Today, advertising aims to sell both necessities and luxury products and to reach the largest number of people possible. Persuasion is the tool of the trade and the key to success.

Check the box next to the correct answer.

1. A new aspect of advertising in modern times is _____ .
   - [ ] a. writing and designing advertisements
   - [ ] b. analyzing the market
   - [ ] c. using persuasion

2. In the 1920s agencies began to investigate _____ .
   - [ ] a. how products could sell themselves
   - [ ] b. how consumers chose products
   - [ ] c. the virtues of new products

3. Advertising agencies have been criticized for _____ .
   - [ ] a. false advertising
   - [ ] b. creating new products
   - [ ] c. conducting consumer research

4. It is unfortunate that today's consumers often base their decisions on

   _____ .
   - [ ] a. the emotional appeal of the packaging
   - [ ] b. motivational research
   - [ ] c. criticism of advertisements

Composition

Look once more at the vacations advertised in the Think and Speak section in Unit 4 of the textbook. Then write a short, unified paragraph telling which of the vacations advertised would appeal to you the most. Before beginning to write, review the information on paragraph structure given in the Composition sections of Units 1 and 2. Then follow the specifications below in constructing your paragraph.

Topic sentence: I would really enjoy taking the vacation to (Kenya) that was advertised by (East Africa Tours).

Supporting sentences: Tell what features of the trip make it attractive to you.

Conclusion: Summarize your feelings about taking such a trip.

_____
_____
_____
_____
_____
_____
_____
_____
_____
_____

Word Game

A. Name at least seven fruits containing the letter *a*.

apple _____ _____ _____
_____ _____ _____

B. List the five months of the year containing the letter *m*.

May _____ _____ _____

C. Think of the names of at least six major cities containing the letter *o*.

Tokyo _____ _____ _____
_____ _____ _____

Unit 6

Complete

An international company has _____ various vacancies. Marilyn
Evans is _____ for a job at the _____ office of the
company.

Marilyn:	I saw your ____ in the paper and _____ like to apply for a _____ .
Interviewer:	What job are you _____ in?
Marilyn:	Do you have any openings in _____ relations?
Interviewer:	What experience _____ you had?
Marilyn:	I _____ as a ticket agent for an airline _____ three years.
Interviewer:	Was that a public relations _____ ?
Marilyn:	Not _____ , but there was a certain _____ of public relations involved. I had to talk to our _____ when we had overbooked a _____ and couldn't take all the _____ with confirmed reservations. Was that _____ difficult!
Interviewer:	I _____ imagine. So how did you _____ a situation _____ that?
Marilyn:	I explained _____ overbooking was an accepted _____ to compensate for "no _____ ." I told them we would _____ another flight and provide _____ meals.

Interviewer: How relieved they _____ have been! But this _____ is a bit different. It calls _____ writing press releases and handling _____ that visit our plant.

Marilyn: I _____ write well. I had to _____ all the department memos _____ . And don't you _____ my experience _____ customers at the airline _____ be helpful in other _____ dealing with the _____ ?

Interviewer: That's _____ , but I think the company _____ more specific experience in public _____ .

Marilyn: I'd like to apply _____ , if that's all _____ .

Interviewer: O.K. Fill _____ this application. You have a _____ , don't you?

Marilyn: Yes, and I have _____ of recommendation _____ the airline.

Interviewer: O.K. _____ you attach them _____ the application?

Write

A. Complete these sentences with the appropriate negative auxiliaries.

1. _____*Can't*_____ you do that tomorrow?
   I think I can.

2. _____ I need to get a physical examination if I took that job?
   Yes, you would.

3. _____ the island of Martinique a part of France?
   I'm sure it is.

4. _____ Sol finished cleaning out the garage yet?
   No, he hasn't.

5. _____ Johnny spill the milk if he serves himself?
   Of course he won't.

6. _____ Alice have taken the wrong train?
   I suppose she could have.

7. _____ we had a wonderful time?
   Yes, we have.

8. _____ we lock the door before we leave?
   I guess we should.

B. Change these statements first to negative exclamations, and then to affirmative exclamations using <u>ever</u>.

1. This has been a pleasant afternoon.
   Hasn't this been a pleasant afternoon!
   Has this ever been a pleasant afternoon!

2. It was nice of the Hansons to invite us to the movie.
   _____!
   _____!

3. That movie was interesting.
   _____!
   _____!

4. That actress is beautiful.
   _____!
   _____!

5. It would be fun to go again next week.
   _____!
   _____!

6. The Hansons are friendly.
   _____!
   _____!

7. We've had a good time today.
   _____!
   _____!

8. It will be nice to get home finally, though.
   _____!
   _____!

C. Change these statements to exclamations with <u>what</u> or <u>how</u>. Use <u>what</u> if a noun phrase is underlined and <u>how</u> if an adjective is underlined.

1. This is <u>an excellent camera</u>.
   What an excellent camera this is!

2. The photograph is <u>beautiful</u>.
   How beautiful the photograph is!

3. Tim told <u>a lie</u>.
   _____!

4. Tim is <u>dishonest</u>.

   _____!

5. Susan had <u>a terrible accident</u>.

_____!

6. She was very <u>scared</u>.

_____!

7. That's <u>a beautiful rose</u>.

_____!

8. It smells <u>nice</u>.

_____!

Listen

A. Listen carefully to the information. Then check the box next to the statement that is true according to the information you have heard.

1. ☐ a. Walter got the job.
   ☐ b. Walter quit his old job.
   ☐ c. Walter has a good chance of getting the job.

2. ☐ a. Tom worked for a shipping company.
   ☐ b. Tom worked for an airline.
   ☐ c. Tom worked for a railroad company.

3. ☐ a. She has experience in public relations.
   ☐ b. She has experience in administration.
   ☐ c. She has experience as a travel agent.

4. ☐ a. He didn't make up his mind.
   ☐ b. He changed his mind.
   ☐ c. He wouldn't change his mind.

5. ☐ a. Melissa got the job.
   ☐ b. Melissa didn't get the job.
   ☐ c. Melissa was disappointed with her new job.

6. ☐ a. Jane didn't come to work.
   ☐ b. Jane won't be at work next week.
   ☐ c. We can't come to work next week.

B. Listen carefully to the brief dialogue, or part of a dialogue, and to the question that follows. Then check the box next to the correct answer.

1. ☐ a. An interviewer and a job applicant.
   ☐ b. A customer and a salesperson.
   ☐ c. A professor and a student.

2. ☐ a. At home.
   ☐ b. In an office.
   ☐ c. In a store.

3. ☐ a. She's not sure if she likes it.
   ☐ b. She loves it.
   ☐ c. She doesn't like it.

4. ☐ a. He loves them.
   ☐ b. He enjoys punishing them.
   ☐ c. He doesn't like them because of their bad habits.

Vocabulary in Context

A. Complete the conversation using the correct form and tense of the appropriate idiom from the list below.

keep in mind	have a heart-to-heart talk with
make up one's mind	not have the heart to
change one's mind	have one's heart set on

Dave: I don't know what to do, Ruth. My mother has _____ my becoming a doctor, just like her. I don't _____ tell her that I'm not interested in medicine. What should I do?

Ruth: Have you _____ yet about what you really want to study?

Dave: Well, I may still _____ , but I'm pretty sure I'd like to study engineering.

Ruth: Well, _____ that your mother wants the best for you. Why don't you _____ your mother and tell her exactly how you feel? I'm sure she'll listen carefully.

88

Dave: That's a good idea. I'd better talk to her now, before I
_____ . Thanks, Ruth.

B. Complete the sentences using the correct form of an expression from the list below.

turn down	turn into	turn on	turn over
turn in	turn off	turn out	turn up

1. When the water boiled, I _____ the gas.
2. At the end of the story the thief _____ to be the detective's son.
3. The children loved the story of the caterpillar that _____ a butterfly.
4. When the baby was three months old, she learned how to _____ from one side to the other.
5. The teacher told the students to _____ their papers in an hour.
6. It was getting too dark to read, so I _____ the light.
7. She asked him to _____ the radio because she couldn't hear it.
8. He asked her to _____ the music because it was too loud.

Read

Jazz

A. Jazz is everything from ragtime to mambo, including blues, boogie-woogie, bop, Dixieland, and the music of the big-name swing bands. It is a soulful music that seems to come directly from the heart of a man or woman, and since it is created

89

through improvisation, it is made anew each time it is played or sung and is often not recorded on paper.

The origins of jazz may be found in a number of places—along the New Orleans riverbanks, in the chain gangs and minstrel shows of the American Plantation South, in the Caribbean Islands, or in Black Africa.

Jazz is a special kind of music. The important elements in its making belong to jazz alone. A simple analysis of blues, a style of jazz with all these elements, will clearly show just how special this music is.

The melody in blues, as in all Western music, is based on scales. But in blues, the familiar major scale is modified in the melody so that three notes are always flatted: the E, G, and B become E-flat, G-flat, and B-flat. While the main melody of a blues piece is built on these "blue notes," the harmony of the piece retains the unflatted notes. Your ear quickly picks up this collision of blue notes and regular notes. The result is a dissonant sound, one that you aren't quite comfortable with. It's as though the music is reaching for a note that lies somewhere between the two.

Check the box next to the correct answer.

1. Most jazz is _____ .
   - ☐ a. created by improvisation
   - ☐ b. recorded on paper
   - ☐ c. created by swing bands

2. One of the places jazz originated is _____ .
   - ☐ a. Europe
   - ☐ b. the southern United States
   - ☐ c. the western United States

3. "Blue notes" form part of _____ .
   - ☐ a. the melody
   - ☐ b. the familiar major scale
   - ☐ c. the harmony

4. The collision of blue notes and regular notes causes _____ .
   - ☐ a. unflatted notes
   - ☐ b. dissonant sound
   - ☐ c. a comfortable harmony

B.   Blues is also characterized by a distinctive rhythm. When the music begins, you feel the steady pulsating rhythm of a 2-beat or 4-beat bar in the background. It's the heartbeat of the music, marked by the beating of a drum, the plucking of a bass, or pressure on a piano pedal. Then the melody of the song comes in. The rhythm of the tune is unexpected. The accents seem out of place. You won't find them on the first beat in a 4-beat bar, but rather on the second or third beat. ONE, two, three, four becomes one, TWO, three, four. This irregular accenting is called syncopation. Carried to the extreme, syncopation can even cause the first beat to disappear completely: ONE, two, three, four becomes ——, TWO, three, four. There are many variations of this rhythm, but all are marked by some kind of syncopation.

So far, we have discussed the structure of jazz—the rhythm and melody, both of which you can record on paper. But the final element of jazz, the tonal color, is something harder to define. Tonal color refers to the quality of the musical sounds. Straight tones vibrate. Clear notes shimmer or slide. A mute is added to a trumpet or to a trombone, and pure tones become growls and rasps. Even new and different sounds are added to the music. Bongo drums bring a hollow, thumping sound. Maracas add the sound of dried beans in a hollow gourd. Brushes whisper along the top of a snare drum. Cymbals, Cuban cowbells, and other instruments add their color to the music.

All this, the melody, rhythm, and tonal color, creates the setting for the star of the jazz band, the soloist. The jazz soloist hears this "arrangement" of the piece and proceeds from there to make it his own. He begins with the melody of his solo part, and launches into an intricate embellishment. He improvises by playing the tune with ornaments, figurations, and flourishes of all sorts. He is showing off his musician's skill, his intuitive feeling for music, his creativity, and his good taste.

Check the box next to the correct answer.

1. Syncopation comes from _____ .
   - ☐ a. a very steady rhythm like a heartbeat
   - ☐ b. the disappearance of the rhythm
   - ☐ c. moving the accent to a different beat

2. Tonal color depends on _____ .
   - ☐ a. the types of instruments used
   - ☐ b. how well a musician plays an instrument
   - ☐ c. the loudness of the music

3. The jazz soloist must _____ .
   - ☐ a. create the setting of the music
   - ☐ b. create the melody
   - ☐ c. sing the melody

4. The word closest in meaning to *improvise* is _____ .
   ☐ a. create
   ☐ b. embellish
   ☐ c. show off

Composition

Read the newspaper ad below.

Times • March 5, 1982
HELP WANTED

FLIGHT ATTENDANTS
Airline seeks male and female employees
to train and work as flight attendants on
international flights. Applicants should be
bilingual, have a neat appearance, and
enjoy travel and people. Send applications
to:
  Mr. Francis Bowen
  Intercontinental Airlines
  10 Park Avenue
  New York, N.Y. 10016

Prepare a letter of application to send to Mr. Bowen. The letter will consist of three paragraphs—an introduction, the body, and a conclusion. Follow the outline provided below.

Introduction: • Express your desire to apply for the job.
                 • Mention how you learned of the position.

Body: • Describe your qualifications and related experience.

Conclusion: • Tell him that you look forward to hearing from him.
               • Tell him you would like to have the opportunity of an interview.

Word Game

Have a race with a friend to see who can form the most words from the letters in the two words below. Proper nouns and plural forms of the same word do not count.

public relations

boat
_____   _____   _____   _____
point
_____   _____   _____   _____
late
_____   _____   _____   _____

_____   _____   _____   _____

_____   _____   _____   _____

_____   _____   _____   _____

Unit 7

Complete

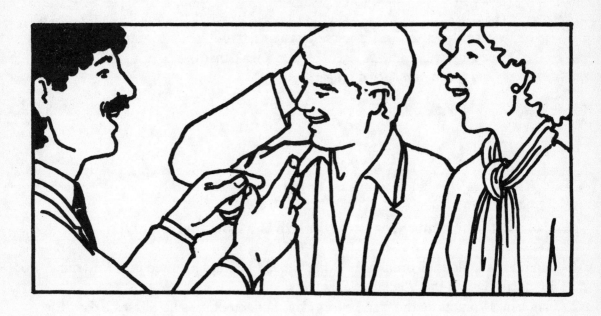

Julia, Alfred, and John have _____ together and are telling each _____ jokes.

John: You're always _____ jokes. Are you sending _____ of them to the joke-writing _____ in the paper?

Julia: I'll tell you _____ , if you promise _____ to use it.

Alfred: O.K. *(John nods in agreement),* we promise. What is ____ ?

Julia: Life is _____ , but what can you always _____ on?

John: I don't _____ . What?

Julia: Your _____ .

Alfred: *(Laughs)* Did you _____ the one about the man _____ buried his car battery _____ the mechanic told him it was _____ ?

Julia: That's a _____ good one. *(Laughs)* John, ____ you have any good _____ to tell?

John: No, but I know some _____ sayings. _____ you like to hear one?

Julia: Sure.

John: "There's nothing _____ with having _____ to say; the trick is _____ to say it _____ ."

Alfred: *(Laughs)* That one is so _____ ! I just remembered
_____ my brother once told me: "_____ to
drive is easy: go when it's _____ , stop when it _____ red, and
slow down _____ your instructor turns _____ ."
(Julia and John Laugh.)

Alfred: *(Laughs)* _____ another one: A _____ is the place
where the _____ nurse insists that you _____ up to take a
sleeping _____ . Isn't that the _____ , though?
(Julia, John and Alfred laugh.)

Write

A. Complete the sentences according to the information given.

1. Sometimes I eat a full breakfast. Other times I just drink coffee in the morning. But
   my doctor insists that *I eat a full breakfast.*

2. Sam usually practices the piano every day, but sometimes he misses a day. His
   teacher prefers that _____
   _____ .

3. Joan hasn't learned to drive a car, but her husband would like her to. Her husband
   suggested that _____
   _____ .

4. Alice doesn't write to a student in a foreign country, but her friend thinks it's a
   good idea. Her friend recommends that _____
   _____ .

5. Jack is seldom on time for work. He's usually twenty minutes late. His boss is
   doing something about it. His boss has demanded that _____
   _____ .

6. Unlike Mrs. Miller, Mr. Miller likes to spend more time at their apartment in the
   city than at their country place. Mrs. Miller prefers that _____
   _____ .

7. Men have to wear a jacket and tie when they go to the restaurant in the Grand
   Hotel. That restaurant requires that _____
   _____ .

8. Mr. Johnson doesn't plan to attend his nephew's wedding, but Mrs. Johnson won't
   let him get away with that. Mrs. Johnson insists that _____
   _____ .

B. Change the following sentences according to the example. Use the words in parentheses.

1. The package must arrive tomorrow.   (urgent)
   It's urgent that the package arrive tomorrow.
2. The doctor must operate immediately.   (imperative)
   _____.
3. Co-workers must cooperate with each other.   (necessary)
   _____.
4. You ought to check the weather report before you go on your trip.   (advisable)
   _____.
5. Children must eat a balanced diet.   (essential)
   _____.
6. Vegetables should be cooked in very little water for the best flavor.   (important)
   _____.
7. Call the office immediately if you are delayed.   (imperative)
   _____.
8. The washing instructions should be followed if you want your clothes to last.   (advisable)
   _____.

C. Write a sentence with <u>always</u> in the present progressive to show a habitual <u>action</u>.

1. Joe catches colds very often.   (forget to wear his coat)
   He's always forgetting to wear his coat.
2. Hal forgets things easily.   (lose umbrella)
   _____.
3. Sharon loves ice cream.   (buy a quart)
   _____.
4. Catherine is very interested in politics.   (write letters to her senator)
   _____.
5. Steve loves clean city streets.   (pick up papers)
   _____.
6. Sally loves word games.   (play Scrabble)
   _____.

D. Write sentences in the present progressive indicating the near future. Use the verbs and time expressions in parentheses.

1. You'd better get ready right away.   (leave the house, in a few minutes)
   We*'re leaving the house in a few minutes*.
2. Sharon ought to finish up her work.   (go on vacation, next week)
   She _____ .
3. They've got to reach the airport by 5:30.   (arrive at 5:45)
   The plane _____ .
4. We really should get home early tonight.   (get up, at 6:00 tomorrow morning)
   We _____ .
5. I have to be there by at least 6:30.   (serve dinner, at 7:00)
   They _____ .
6. Jim's room has to be ready by Friday morning.   (come home, on Saturday)
   He _____ .

E. Fill in the blanks in the following news report using the future progressive form of the verbs below.

meet   leave   join   attend   visit   travel   give   make

The president _____*will be leaving*_____ for a tour of the Far East on Monday.
He _____ on Air Force 1. In Manila he
_____ a conference of leaders of Southeast Asian countries and
_____ a speech before the assembled group. On Wednesday,
the president's wife _____ him in Tokyo, the next stop. The
first family _____ several factories and
_____ with the prime minister on Friday. The president
_____ stops in Singapore and Kuala Lumpur before returning to
Washington on Sunday.

Listen

A. Listen carefully to the information. Then check the box next to the statement that is true according to the information you have heard.

1. ☐ a. Mary has been collecting coins longer than Jim.
   ☐ b. Mary has collected more coins than Jim.
   ☐ c. Jim has collected more coins than Mary.

2. □ a. Lee tells jokes very well.
   □ b. Lee is a comedian.
   □ c. Lee is not a good joke teller.

3. □ a. John probably tells good jokes.
   □ b. The people probably didn't want John to tell jokes.
   □ c. John's jokes are probably not too funy.

4. □ a. The show was a success.
   □ b. The show was a failure.
   □ c. The audience was bored.

5. □ a. Carmen hardly ever talks about herself.
   □ b. Carmen talks about herself too much.
   □ c. Carmen is talking right now.

B. Listen carefully to the brief dialogue, or part of a dialogue, and to the question that follows. Then check the box next to the correct answer.

1. □ a. A bracelet.
   □ b. A knife.
   □ c. A glass.

2. □ a. Allen saw the show.
   □ b. Allen was in the show.
   □ c. Allen didn't like the show.

3. □ a. He found it too difficult to understand.
   □ b. He found it complicated, but he was able to understand it.
   □ c. He found it quite interesting.

4. □ a. She's coming down the stairs.
   □ b. She's getting sick.
   □ c. She's cold.

Vocabulary in Context

A. Complete the sentences using the correct form of the appropriate idiom from the list below.

over one's head   break one's neck
keep one's head   stick one's neck out
go to one's head

Jim: I can't understand why you fired my son.

Jane: I'm sorry, Jim. I tried to give him a chance, but the job was
_____ . I kept telling my boss that he would improve, and
finally I just couldn't _____ for him anymore.

Jim: I'll tell you, Jane, you've changed a lot since you got your promotion. You've
let it _____ .

Jane: Look, Jim, you don't know how hard my job is. I have to
_____ to get the work done, and I try to remain calm and
_____ . But I need workers who can handle the job with
little supervision.

B. Complete the sentences using the correct form of an expression from the list below.

come across   come in   come on
come down with   come off   come over
come from

1. At the party he _____ an old friend.
2. _____ to my house for coffee tomorrow morning.
3. _____ , let's go to the beach.
4. He _____ the South and didn't like the cold winters in New York.
5. After her vacation she _____ a very bad cold.
6. They opened the door and invited all the children to _____ .
7. A button _____ his coat.

Read

Read each joke and the question that follows it. Then check the box next to the correct answer.

A. A farmer was having difficulty with his horse. He wrestled with the reins to stop him and he flapped them wildly to get him to start.

"Look," said Smith, "Why don't you say 'whoa' when you want him to stop and 'giddap' when you want him to go?"

"Listen to me," said the farmer, "that horse kicked me three years ago and if you think I'm going to go asking him for favors, you're mistaken."

The farmer did not want to say anything to his horse because
_____ .
- ☐ a. the horse did not speak English
- ☐ b. the horse kicked him the last time he made a request
- ☐ c. the farmer liked to flap wildly at the horse

B. A traveling show had a knife-throwing act and Stacey went twice to see the fascinating spectacle. When George told her that he was going, she didn't encourage him.

"Don't George," she said, "you'll be wasting your money."

"Why's that?"

"He has a rotten aim. He keeps missing her."

Stacey didn't think George should go see the act because _____ .
- ☐ a. it was too expensive
- ☐ b. it was not very exciting
- ☐ c. the man throwing the knife never hit the woman

C. The farmer showed the city dweller how to milk the cows and sent him into the fields.

"How many did you milk?" he asked when the city dweller came back.

"Twenty, but there's one thing . . ."

"What's that?" the farmer asked.

"I think you should have given me a bucket."

The city dweller _____ back from the fields.
- ☐ a. brought a bucket
- ☐ b. brought the milk from twenty cows
- ☐ c. didn't bring anything

D. Mary's phone rang very early one morning. It was Charlotte who wanted to know the time.

"It's four o'clock in the morning."

"Thanks," said Charlotte, "I hope I didn't disturb you."

"Not a bit. I had to get up to answer the phone anyway."

Mary had to get up _____ .

- ☐ a. to go to work
- ☐ b. to answer the phone
- ☐ c. to find out the time

E. There was a part of the country where the train service was not as good as it should be. On one occasion a tourist complained about the slowness of the train.

"Why don't you get off and walk?" asked the harassed conductor.

"Because I'm not in that big of a hurry."

The tourist claimed that _____ .

- ☐ a. the conductor was very harassed
- ☐ b. he should get off and walk
- ☐ c. walking was faster than taking the train

Composition

A. The school year is about to end, and you are planning to take a two-week trip as soon as classes are over. You would like to invite a good friend to go along with you. Write your friend a letter. In the first paragraph, talk about your activities in your final days at school. In the second paragraph, describe the place you are going to visit. In the third paragraph, try to convince your friend to go with you. The topic sentences are provided for each paragraph.

_____ ,

The school year is almost over, and I'm busier than ever. _____

_____

_____

_____

_____
_____
_____
_____

   I'm planning a trip to (   ) this summer. They say it's a fabulous
place to visit. _____
_____
_____
_____
_____
_____

   Why don't you come with me? It would be a lot of fun. _____
_____
_____
_____
_____
_____

   Please write back as soon as you can.

                                            _____ ,
                                            _____

Word Game

Below are two lists of words. Read the words in the column on the left and then try to match each one with a related word from the column on the right. Look for words which are antonyms, synonyms, or which belong to the same categories.

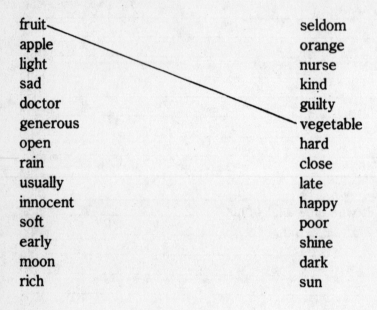

fruit	seldom
apple	orange
light	nurse
sad	kind
doctor	guilty
generous	vegetable
open	hard
rain	close
usually	late
innocent	happy
soft	poor
early	shine
moon	dark
rich	sun

Unit 8

Complete

Ralph Cole, Ophelia Martin, and Betty Spencer _____ friends. They're
_____ informally in the lounge of a _____ library. They're
_____ their reading likes and _____ .

Ralph: _____ I need is a good _____ story, and I'm perfectly
happy _____ the evening. I like a story _____ a fast-moving
_____ , a book that I can't put _____ until I finish.

Ophelia: _____ can you like such action-filled _____ ? There's
_____ there. Somebody kills _____ else, the sad-
faced detective looks for _____ , and eventually finds the _____
because it wasn't a perfect _____ after all. ____ human conflict, no
_____ development, no esthetic experience. _____
bang, bang, you're _____ , and crime doesn't _____ .

Betty: I don't know, because I _____ read many detective stories.
But I _____ I wouldn't like science _____ until I read
some _____ good novels by people _____ Ursula Le Guin and
Arthur C. Clarke. I find that _____ when the setting is _____
space, the stories are _____ about human experiences and feelings.

Ralph: _____ fiction is too complicated _____ me. Maybe you want
to speculate _____ life ten thousand years _____ now, but I

105

want _____ simple—the good _____ and the bad guys. Besides, you do _____ a lot about people in a good _____ story. Everyone has a different _____ for doing something, _____ wanting to kill someone. But who _____ it? That's what's _____ for me.

Ophelia: That may _____ so, but a great _____ like Hemingway's *The _____ Also Rises* tells you _____ than who did what. It _____ you how people's experiences _____ their lives. Maybe that's escape too, _____ I think you can really _____ something from trying _____ imagine what you would do in _____ else's shoes. Or even _____ you might feel if you _____ in a different time and _____ .

Betty: I don't think the _____ of a novel is too _____ . I think a good _____ can make almost _____ interesting. Isn't it really the writer's _____ of language that makes something _____ reading?

Ralph: Well, it's _____ for me just to find _____ who committed the _____ and how the detective _____ it out.

Write

A. Answer the questions with hyphenated modifiers.

1. What do you call a record that plays a long time?
   A long-playing record.
2. What do you call a curve that is shaped like a bell?
   A bell-shaped curve.
3. What do you call a person who has thin skin?

   _____.
4. What do you call a baby with blue eyes?

   _____.
5. What do you call an oven that cleans itself?

   _____.
6. What do you call a person who moves slowly?

   _____.
7. What do you call a factory that is operated by computer?

   _____.
8. What do you call a voice with a high pitch?

   _____.

9. What do you call a person who means well?

_____.

10. What do you call a person who is always dressed well?

_____.

B. Rewrite these definitions so that they use hyphenated modifiers.

1. The earth is a planet shaped like a pear.
   The earth is a pear-shaped planet.
2. A hexagon is a figure with six sides.

_____.

3. A horse is an animal with four legs.

_____.

4. Plastic is a material made by man.

_____.

5. A bigot is a person with a narrow mind.

_____.

6. An aristocrat is a person with blue blood.

_____.

C. Write a description of the following characters using the information given in the form of hyphenated modifiers.

Blanche: looks funny, talks fast, has a loud mouth, chews gum.
Al: looks dangerous, has two faces, drinks hard, has a strong will.
Frank: looks ridiculous, has sleepy eyes, smokes a pipe, loves peace.

1. Blanche is a ____*funny-looking*____ , _____ ,
   _____ , _____ woman.
2. Al is a _____ , _____ ,
   _____ , _____ bum.
3. Frank is a _____ , _____ ,
   _____ , _____ guy.

Listen

A. Listen carefully to the information. Then check the box next to the statement that is true according to the information you have heard.

1. ☐ a. Jason is bad-tempered.
   ☐ b. Jason is bad-mannered.
   ☐ c. Jason is good-tempered.

2. ☐ a. Anne is right-handed.
   ☐ b. Anne writes with her left hand.
   ☐ c. Anne has small hands.

3. ☐ a. Lucille makes me nervous.
   ☐ b. I make Lucille nervous.
   ☐ c. Something makes Lucille nervous.

4. ☐ a. I know Jane missed the plane.
   ☐ b. Jane probably missed the plane.
   ☐ c. Jane's plane isn't here yet.

5. ☐ a. The woman looked dangerous.
   ☐ b. The woman looked surprised.
   ☐ c. The woman looked nice.

B. Listen carefully to the brief dialogue, or part of a dialogue, and to the question that follows. Then check the box next to the correct answer.

1. ☐ a. At a school.
   ☐ b. At a store.
   ☐ c. At a party.

2. ☐ a. A conservative person.
   ☐ b. A happy person.
   ☐ c. A long-haired person.

3. ☐ a. He had a dental exam.
   ☐ b. He passed his driving exam.
   ☐ c. He failed an exam.

4. ☐ a. He taught himself.
   ☐ b. He taught many people.
   ☐ c. He taught many subjects.

Vocabulary in Context

A. Complete the sentences using the correct form of the appropriate idiom from the list below.

> by the skin of one's teeth   let one's hair down
> get on someone's nerves   split hairs

Jack: I won fifty dollars! The horse I bet on just made it

_____ !

Roberta: It _____ to see you waste money on horses, Jack. You say you can stop when you want to, but I know you can't.

Jack: But it's not a waste of money. Sometimes I just need to relax and _____ . There's a difference between going to the races to win money and going there for relaxation.

Roberta: You're just _____ , Jack. You can't face the truth. The fact is, you already owe money to me and to everybody we know.

B. Complete the sentences using the correct form of an expression from the list below.

keep away from	keep off	keep out of
keep back	keep on	keep up

1. "Restrain them, please! _____ them _____ !" the zoo attendant said to the police officer when she saw the crowds who had come to see the new baby elephant.

2. The attendant then called out to the visitors: "This baby needs to sleep, and it's not good to _____ him _____ . You must _____ the fence, and _____ the yard.

3. He's shy. You'll even have to _____ the walk surrounding his building because he'll be nervous. But if you _____ walking up the hill, you'll see him very well from there."

Read

Pandas

A.   More than 4,000 years ago, the Chinese Emperor Yu paid tribute to a magnificent beast: a bear-like creature with black markings on his white fur coat. For the next 2,500 years, all reference to this creature vanished, until, in 650 A.D., Chinese manuscripts told of the white bear from the mountainous bamboo forests.

How did this great creature remain hidden for so many centuries? The answer is not so surprising when we read the chronicle of the first Western man who captured a giant panda just over 100 years ago. Père Armand David, a French

missionary-explorer, set out for the wilds of Western China in search of rare plants and animals, including the "great white bear."

The western regions of China were inhospitable to explorers. The panda's home, the almost impenetrable bamboo forests of the rugged mountainsides, was surely the most brutal part of all. Père David, like others before and after him, had to fight the rough terrain, the bitter weather, and the threat of unfriendly native tribes. These surroundings, however, were well suited to the giant panda. He could live alone comfortably. The bamboo provided a nutritious and steady diet, and its thick growth formed a sturdy shield against the bitter winters.

In 1869, Père David and his men found and captured a giant panda. David might have guessed at some of the attention that the panda would later claim. He realized that the panda had highly unusual physical characteristics and was probably a new species. David wrote that he thought this must be some "new species of bear." In Paris, examiners looked closely at the skins and skeleton and guessed that this "new bear" was not a bear at all, but instead a kind of raccoon. So began the genealogical debate that continues even today.

Check the box next to the correct answer.

1. The panda was undiscovered for many centuries because _____ .
   ☐ a. he is very shy
   ☐ b. his homeland is hard to explore
   ☐ c. no one knew he existed

2. The bamboo forest is better suited for the giant panda than for man because
_____ .
- [ ] a. it lies on the rough mountain slopes
- [ ] b. there is bitter weather in that region
- [ ] c. bamboo is a staple in the pandas' diets

3. Père David was especially excited by his discovery because
_____ .
- [ ] a. it was the sole purpose of his expedition
- [ ] b. he guessed the panda was a new species
- [ ] c. he recognized the pandas' fur could make him wealthy

4. In the genealogical debate over pandas it is said that _____ .
- [ ] a. pandas are a new species of raccoon
- [ ] b. pandas are a new species of bear
- [ ] c. both a. and b.

B.   Although the background and origins of the panda may remain obscure for a long time, the pandas in captivity in the West have given us a clear picture of the character, habits, and tastes of this animal. Because of his size and strength, a panda is a potentially frightful and awesome beast. But his clumsy and uncoordinated ways make him an awkward and defensive creature. He fumbles along, pigeon-toed, in an ungraceful, diagonal walk. He is rarely urged from this lumbering pace. Only a young panda, or a panda in desperate flight, will venture to climb a tree. And once he has reached the top, it becomes an even greater task to get down.

The panda's personality is also in ironic contrast to his appearance. The panda has been described as shy and timid. Panda watchers at the zoo are often disappointed by the lack of playful spirit in this lovable bear. Water does not tempt him to frolic. In fact, the panda will shy away from bathing as long as possible and then go to great lengths to avoid immersing himself in water. However, many a panda has been seen sleeping contentedly upon a big slab of ice. It is not surprising that this slow-moving and easy-going panda spends most of his time sleeping.

Despite his aloof manner and clumsiness, the giant panda has won a reputation as a loving and adorable creature. With his big, furry head, gentle flat face, and dark-ringed sad eyes, the giant panda is irresistible. His lopsided movements and his timidity have endeared him to countless friends and admirers at zoos around the world. But unfortunately for humans, there are so few pandas that the supply cannot meet the demand. Thus, many of us must be content to know them only through representations—as toy bears, on posters or cards, and in books, cartoons, and films.

Check the box next to the correct answer.

1. The panda's size and strength _____ .
   - ☐ a. make him a dangerous and frightful animal
   - ☐ b. become a handicap by making him awkward
   - ☐ c. helped him ward off hunters and explorers for many centuries

2. Panda watchers at the zoo are often disappointed because
   _____ .
   - ☐ a. the panda walks pigeon-toed at a lumbering pace
   - ☐ b. the panda spends most of his time sleeping
   - ☐ c. the panda is lovable looking but lacks a playful spirit

3. The world is fond of pandas because _____ .
   - ☐ a. their oversized and awkward shape makes them lovable
   - ☐ b. they are playful and venturesome and responsive to audiences
   - ☐ c. they have rarely been seen in person

4. Many people must be content to know pandas through representations because
   _____ .
   - ☐ a. pandas are too shy and timid to be displayed at zoos
   - ☐ b. there are not enough pandas to meet the demand at zoos
   - ☐ c. pandas are dangerous and difficult to keep

Composition

A. A good composition consists of three parts:
   1. **An introduction: a paragraph introducing the topic.**
   2. **A discussion: several paragraphs dealing with various aspects of the topic.**
   3. **A conclusion: a paragraph summarizing the main points made in the discussion paragraphs.**

Read carefully the passage in the Read section on p. 70. Locate the

main idea, expressed in one sentence, for each paragraph, and write the sentences in the spaces provided below.

Introduction: _____

_____

Discussion:
Paragraph 1: _____

_____

Paragraph 2: _____

_____

Paragraph 3: _____

_____

Paragraph 4: _____

_____

Conclusion: _____

_____

B. Read the following poem carefully.

Two Kinds of People

There are two kinds of people on earth today,
Just two kinds of people, no more, I say,
Not the good and the bad, for 'tis well understood
The good are half bad and the bad are half good.

Not the happy and sad, for the swift flying years
Bring each man his laughter and each man his tears.
Not the rich and the poor, for to count a man's wealth
You must first know the state of his conscience and health.

Not the humble and proud, for in life's busy span
Who puts on vain airs is not counted a man.
No! The two kinds of people on earth I mean
Are the people who lift, and the people who lean.

Wherever you go you will find the world's masses
Are ever divided in just these two classes.
And, strangely enough, you will find, too, I wean,
There is only one lifter to twenty who lean.

This one question I ask. Are you easing the load
Of overtaxed lifters who toil down the road?
Or are you a leaner who lets others bear
Your portion of worry and labor and care?

Author: Ella Wheeler Wilcox, American poet and novelist
Born: In 1850 at Johnstown Centre, Wisconsin
Died: October 31, 1919 in England

Now write a three-paragraph composition about the poem following the outline below.

Introduction: Identify the poem and its author and give a brief biographical sketch using the information supplied after the poem.

Discussion: Explain the topic of the poem and the poet's message.

Conclusion: Describe your reaction to the poem. Did you like it or dislike it? Why?

Word Game

Next to each word, write a homonym—a word which sounds the same, but has a different spelling.

1. witch	*which*	8. rode		
2. roll		9. scene		
3. add		10. site		
4. break		11. hare		
5. maid		12. plain		
6. weak		13. fair		
7. stares		14. hear		

114

Unit 9

Complete

Christine, Donald, and Roger _____ momentarily. Christine tells them _____ the poetry reading she _____ last night.

Donald: Hi Christine! Caroline said she _____ you at the poetry _____ last night. Did you _____ it?

Christine: It was _____ of the best I've _____ attended. The auditorium was _____ to capacity.

Roger: _____ poetry did they read?

Christine: First _____ was a poem by Robert Frost. _____ there were several of Emily Dickinson's, and the _____ poems were by Carl Sandburg. Are you _____ with anything they _____ ?

Donald: Well, I _____ Robert Frost's "Stopping by Woods _____ a Snowy Evening" in high _____ .

Roger: I remember reading somewhere _____ Emily Dickinson lived almost _____ a hermit. And furthermore, she was _____ unknown until after her _____ .

Christine: That's right. Only seven of her _____ were published during her _____ . When she died, they _____ nearly two thousand poems hidden _____ in her desk.

Roger: _____ of Carl Sandburg's poems did they read?

Christine: They read my favorite _____ , "Chicago."

Roger: Do you know any poems _____ heart?

Christine: Just a _____ .

Donald: Have you written any poetry _____ ?

Christine: Yes. But I'd be _____ embarrassed to let _____ read it. . . .

Donald: Oh, come _____ , Christine. Read us a few of _____ poems.

Christine: Maybe sometime I _____ . However, if you're interested _____ really good poetry, why _____ you come to the next _____ reading?

Donald: When is _____ ?

Christine: Next Thursday night at eight, _____ the Civic Center. You've _____ to get there _____ seven thirty, though, _____ you want to get a good _____ .

Donald: O.K.! I'll come. . . . How _____ you Roger?

Roger: I'll think _____ it and let you _____ .

Write

A. Paul has bought paint and is ready to paint his room. Write some instructions for him by putting the steps below in order and using sequence words such as first, second, third, next, then, last, finally, and last of all.

protect the floor
remove the furniture
remove the switch plates
tape the woodwork
stir the paint
clean the walls
paint the walls

First, remove the furniture from the room. _____

_____

_____

_____

_____

116 _____

B. Divide the ideas in these sentences in two. Use the relating words given in parentheses.

1. Michael speaks French, German, and Swedish, and reads Russian and Polish.　(in addition)
   Michael speaks French, German, and Swedish. In addition, he reads Russian and Polish.

2. Sam ate fried chicken, potato salad, bread, vegetables, and pie for dessert.　(moreover)
   _____

   _____

3. The museum contains paintings, drawings, sculpture, and a wonderful cafeteria.　(also)
   _____

   _____

4. I want that letter written, typed, stamped, mailed, and in the post office tonight!　(furthermore)
   _____

   _____

5. Take light clothing, rest after lunch, don't carry money, and send postcards.　(also)
   _____

   _____

6. I don't like the style and I refuse to pay more than forty dollars for a dress.　(moreover)
   _____

   _____

C. Make an opposing comment about these statements. Use the relating words given in parentheses.

1. Skiing is a lot of fun.　(however)
   However, ski equipment is expensive.

2. Doughnuts are delicious.　(but)
   _____.

3. Football is a healthy sport.　(nevertheless)
   _____.

4. Guayaquil, Ecuador is very hot.　(but)
   _____.

5. Instant coffee is convenient.　(on the other hand)
   _____.

6. Computers can work very fast.   (nevertheless)

_____.

7. Pizza originated in Italy.   (however)

_____.

8. Haiti is a nice country.   (nevertheless)

_____.

9. It takes a long time to become a doctor.   (on the other hand)

_____.

10. Latin is a dead language.   (however)

_____.

Listen

A. Listen carefully to the information. Then check the box next to the statement that is true according to the information you have heard.

1. ☐ a. Robert got a good bargain.
   ☐ b. Robert paid too much for the car.
   ☐ c. Robert's car was very expensive.

2. ☐ a. Neither Edgar nor Stella likes to discuss poetry.
   ☐ b. Edgar and Stella don't agree about the meaning of poems.
   ☐ c. Edgar and Stella have the same ideas about poems.

3. ☐ a. Steven took up Turkish.
   ☐ b. Steven took on Turkish.
   ☐ c. Steven took down Turkish.

4. ☐ a. Sarah got the job.
   ☐ b. Michael didn't know if Sarah got the job.
   ☐ c. Sarah didn't get the job.

B. Listen carefully to the brief dialogue, or part of a dialogue, and to the question that follows. Then check the box next to the correct answer.

1. ☐ a. A lawyer.   2. ☐ a. Two.
   ☐ b. A patient.   ☐ b. Three.
   ☐ c. A doctor.   ☐ c. Four.

3. ☐ a. Understand poetry.
   ☐ b. Read poetry aloud.
   ☐ c. Read poetry with expression.

4. ☐ a. Both Sharon and Mark.
   ☐ b. Sharon only.
   ☐ c. Mark only.

Vocabulary in Context

A. Complete the sentences using the correct tense of the appropriate idiom from the list below.

pay through the nose   be up to one's ears
catch someone's eye   see eye to eye
play it by ear

"I tried to _____ when I saw you talking to Steve about buying his old car. I didn't want you to make a quick decision and then have to _____ for it. I wanted you just to discuss the matter with him casually and then _____ until you are sure that all of your family would _____ with you on the decision. Otherwise, you could _____ in problems."

B. Complete the sentence using the correct form of an expression from the list below.

take after   take off   take over
take down   take on   take up
take in

1. After six hours of studying, my mind was too tired to _____ any more names and dates.
2. I decided to _____ playing the flute.
3. When the boss retires next year, her son will _____ the company.
4. He couldn't _____ more work because he was about to leave for his vacation.
5. She said she'd feel better if she could _____ a few days to rest.
6. If my children _____ me, they'll need glasses at the age of fifteen.
7. She pulled out a pencil and paper and tried to _____ the number of the license plate on his car as he drove away.

Read

The Craft of the Winemaker

A.   In the river valleys around the globe, Nature and the winemaker work together to produce the world's great varieties of wines. Nature provides the favorable elements of climate to grow the fat, round grapes. The winemaker, skilled in a craft that requires both precision and sensitive intuition, supervises the aging and blending of the juice. The end product, the wine, finds its way to winelovers everywhere.

All wines, from the brilliant Bordeaux to the hearty Chiantis, are produced by the same time-tested principles. The grapes are grown in fertile soil in temperate climates. At harvest, they are picked individually or in bunches. The grapes, complete with skin and seeds, are pressed into juice. The liquid, called "must," is poured into great wooden casks to ferment. During this fermentation process, the yeast in the grape skin acts on the sugar in the grape juice to change it into alcohol. Although wines can be made from any kinds of fruits and vegetables—from plums to parsnips—all but one require some artificial additives during fermentation. Only grapes contain the proper amounts of the vital ingredients—sugar, yeast, and water—for natural fermentation.

After several weeks in the wooden casks, the fermented wine is strained and bottled, and the bottles are then stored on their sides in cool caves. The aging process begins. It can last from one month to sometimes over 100 years. Not all wines can withstand a long aging process, and many wines must be drunk while they are still young. There are some wines, however, that seem to improve almost indefinitely with age.

Check the box next to the correct answer.

1. The "must" is _____ .
   - ☐ a. unfermented juice
   - ☐ b. the grape skin
   - ☐ c. a type of yeast

2. During the fermentation process, _____ .
   - ☐ a. yeast is changed into alcohol
   - ☐ b. sugar is changed into alcohol
   - ☐ c. yeast is changed into juice

3. Among the fruits used to make wine, grapes _____ .
   - ☐ a. are not as good as some others
   - ☐ b. require artificial additives
   - ☐ c. are the only ones that contain all the necessary ingredients

4. _____ wines can be aged indefinitely.
   - ☐ a. All
   - ☐ b. No
   - ☐ c. Some

B. Variations on the basic winemaking process result in the different colors, tastes, and types of wines. Red wine comes from red grapes. White wine comes from white grapes, or from red if the skin and seeds are removed from the juice before fermentation. Rosé, or pink wine, is made from red grapes whose skins are removed from the "must" early in the fermentation process. As for taste, a change in harvest time can alter the sweetness of the final wine. The riper the grapes are when they are picked, the more sugar they contain. When most of the sugar in the grapes is fermented to alcohol, the resulting wine is "dry." But when more sugar is left unfermented, the wine is "sweet."

Other techniques are used to produce the various types of wine. Sparkling wine is a carbonated red or white wine that is fermented beyond the normal point by adding sugar and yeast; this gives it its bubbly character. Fortified wines, like sherry from Spain, are a blend of old and new vintages of wine. An aromatic wine, such as vermouth, is a white wine flavored with herbs and roots that give it its distinctive bouquet. Portugal's port wine is red wine fermented in casks containing brandy.

Today many wines are named for the regions where they are made. France is famed for the clarets of Bordeaux; the light, dry red wines from Burgundy; and the sweet, white wines from Sauternes. In Germany, the valleys of the Rhine and Moselle produce white wines from rich, full-bodied sweet to light dry. Italy is well known both for its Chianti, a rough, dry wine from the Tuscany region, and for its sweet and dry vermouth. In the United States, large varieties of wines bear the labels of the vineyards of northern California and New York.

Check the box next to the correct answer.

1. If the skins of red grapes are removed from the "must" during fermentation, _____ wine results.
   - ☐ a. white
   - ☐ b. red
   - ☐ c. rosé

2. A dry wine is produced by _____ .
   - ☐ a. picking the grapes early
   - ☐ b. fermenting most of the grape sugar
   - ☐ c. by adding sugar to the "must"

3. Some special techniques produce wines such as _____ .
   - ☐ a. sparkling wine, sherry, and brandy
   - ☐ b. sherry, port, and vermouth
   - ☐ c. vintages, vermouth, and port

4. The names of wines usually depend on _____ .
   - ☐ a. the region where they're produced
   - ☐ b. their sweetness or dryness
   - ☐ c. the technique used to produce them

Composition

Write a three-paragraph composition on your favorite novel.

Introduction: Identify the novel and its author and give a brief introduction to the novel.

Discussion: Summarize the plot of the novel and tell about some of the novel's important features.

Conclusion: Describe your reaction to the novel. Why do you like it?

Word Game

Match the words in column one with the words in columns two and three which contain the same vowel sound.

I	II	III
name	father	hotel
pop	sample	scene
law	think	shine
man	bribe	slate
soap	key	caught
sky	rain	hot
dinner	talk	mitten
beef	cove	candle

Unit 10

Complete

Martha Fong and Oscar Sebastian are professional _____ , conversing informally at a friend's _____ . They have been _____ the things they studied in _____ . They disagree about the _____ of their writing lessons. Surprisingly, Martha, who _____ very well, is against too _____ emphasis on writing, and Oscar, who _____ about problems in writing, would require _____ writing practice.

Oscar: I'm constantly having ____ write letters, reports, notes, notices, and _____ essays. I wish my teachers _____ made me write more ____ college. I just hate to sit _____ and write now. In other _____ , I can't put down on _____ what I think. It always comes _____ scrambled. I can't even _____ very well.

Martha: That's funny. I think my teachers _____ me write too much, even in my _____ classes. In fact, I spent ____ much time writing that I _____ had enough time to master the _____ matter, and that's what _____ if you want to become an engineer.

Oscar: But that's not _____ that counts. You'd think that ____ engineer only needs to _____ math, science, and that _____ of thing, but everybody _____ to write letters, take _____ , and write memos and reports of one _____ or another. And I find it ____ difficult that I simply _____ it.

124

Martha: But notes and letters are _____ to write. And you can always get _____ to write an occasional report.

Oscar: Yes. Notes and letters _____ easy to write. But write a note to your _____ and misspell a word, and see _____ happens to his opinion of _____ . You may be the _____ engineer in the company, but _____ confidence in you might ____ shaken.

Martha: But you can look ____ words in the dictionary. You _____ have to do that, _____ you have a secretary who's __ good speller.

Oscar: It's not _____ simple. For instance, you don't know _____ words you're going to _____ , so you either look up _____ word, which is totally impractical, ____ you misspell a few words. And _____ your best friends won't tell _____ about your spelling mistakes. Besides, ____ they did, you'd probably _____ embarrassed or resentful.

Write

Rewrite the following groups of sentences by adding an appropriate introductory expression before the last statement. If the last statement summarizes, add in short or in other words. If the last statement is an example, add for instance or for example.

1. My trip to Miami was so relaxing. I went to the beach every day and met some really nice people. I had a marvelous time.
   My trip to Miami was so relaxing. I went to the beach every day and met some really nice people. In short (In other words), I had a marvelous time.
2. New York is a great city to visit. There's so much to do and see there. You can go the theater, the ballet, or the opera almost any night of the week.
   New York is a great city to visit. There's so much to do and see there. For example (For instance), you can go to the theater, the ballet, or the opera almost any night of the week.
3. Mr. and Mrs. Sampson haven't been getting along well. They've had terrible arguments and have been living apart for periods of time. They're having serious marital problems.

   _____

   _____

   _____

4. Nancy's husband has been in the hospital for several weeks. She has a family at home to take care of and she has to stay late at the office almost every night. She's under a lot of pressure.

_____

_____

_____

5. The boss doesn't want us to have a New Year's party at the office. He says the employees will be too noisy and that it will cost him too much to buy the food and drinks. We can forget the whole idea.

_____

_____

_____

6. Politicians really irritate me. They make promises and then forget them when they are elected to office. Before our mayor was elected, he said he'd improve the schools, but nothing has been done yet.

_____

_____

_____

7. If you want to do something useful for your community, you can always do volunteer work. There are many public institutions which need people to help. You can be a volunteer fire fighter.

_____

_____

_____

8. There are many different ways to make money in your spare time. There are several things you can do in your own home. You can sell magazine subscriptions by telephone.

_____

_____

_____

9. Some communities are making a real effort to beautify their streets. A local neighborhood association has just planted flowers along several blocks.

_____

_____

_____

10. Unemployment is rising rapidly. Usually unemployment slows inflation. Nevertheless, the government is having a hard time keeping inflation under control. The economy is in deep trouble.

_____

_____

_____

Listen

A. Listen carefully to the information. Then check the box next to the statement that is true according to the information you have heard.

1. ☐ a. An engineer only needs to know math and computer problems.
   ☐ b. Everybody, even engineers, needs to know how to write.
   ☐ c. Everybody, except engineers, needs to know how to write.

2. ☐ a. Steven earns extra money by selling newspapers.
   ☐ b. Steve earns his living by working at a newsstand.
   ☐ c. Steve spends his extra money at a newsstand.

3. ☐ a. The policemen were arguing.
   ☐ b. The argument was turning into a fight.
   ☐ c. The argument wasn't serious.

4. ☐ a. Lisa and Stacey resemble Mary and Susan.
   ☐ b. Lisa and Stacey are twins.
   ☐ c. Lisa and Stacey look alike.

5. ☐ a. Mrs. Martin has plenty of extra time.
   ☐ b. Mrs. Martin is busy all the time.
   ☐ c. Mrs. Martin is carrying things in her hands.

B. Listen to the brief dialogue, or part of a dialogue, and to the question that follows. Then check the box next to the correct answer.

1. ☐ a. An interviewer and a job applicant.
   ☐ b. A student and a professor.
   ☐ c. A doctor and a professor.

2. ☐ a. They couldn't put out the fire because of the crowd.
   ☐ b. The crowd helped fight the fire.
   ☐ c. The crowd made it difficult for them to put out the fire.

3. ☐ a. That the trip was cheap.
   ☐ b. That the trip was reasonable.
   ☐ c. That the trip was expensive.

4. ☐ a. In short.
   ☐ b. For example.
   ☐ c. First.

Vocabulary in Context

A. Complete the conversation using the correct form of the appropriate idiom from the list below.

out of hand	put one's foot in one's mouth
put one's foot down	cost an arm and a leg
pull one's leg	have one's hands full

Ellen: Everything here is really getting _____ .
You know I _____ getting the surprise anniversary party ready for Alice and Mark. Well, the children just came home and announced that they're having lunch here because for some reason school is out for the rest of the day. And now you've come in for lunch. I've got to _____ and say, "No, I can't."

William: But I didn't come for lunch. I came to tell you that Alice and Mark are both sick. It's contagious, but not serious. The doctor says they can't go out.

Ellen: Come on, Will, you're _____ .

William: No, I'm really serious. In fact, I almost
_____ by laughing when Alice's daughter told me about it. I was thinking of the party, of course.

Ellen: I could cry.

William: Come on, Ellen, don't let it get you down.
It's really quite funny, in a way.

Ellen: Funny! Do you have any idea what this party has cost us? It's

_____ .

William: We can keep the party things, and we'll just eat ice cream cake for
breakfast, lunch, and dinner for the next three weeks.

B. Complete the sentences using the correct form of an expression from the list below.

look around	look forward to	look like
look down on	look into	look up

1. She told him that she would _____ the matter before making a final decision.
2. You shouldn't _____ other people when you think you know more than they do about something.
3. I always use the wrong name when I introduce Lucy to people, because she _____ her cousin Carol.
4. If you don't understand a word, you should _____ it _____ in the dictionary.
5. He _____ the party because all his friends would be there.
6. When I'm in a new city, I like to _____ a while before planning what I want to do.

Read

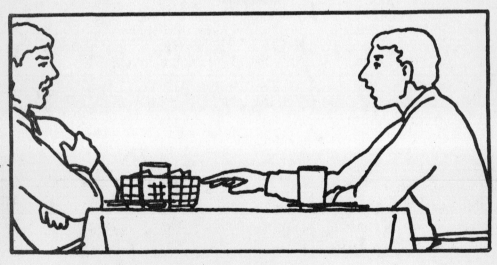

Space Talks

A.   Imagine this scene—Alex is chatting with his friend Bill at a restaurant. The small table is set and the two friends are waiting for dinner. It has been a long, exhausting day, and Alex is still trying to relax. Without thinking, he starts to fiddle with the items on the table. First he moves the salt shaker toward Bill.

Alex's movement catches Bill's eye, but Bill continues to talk, unbothered. Then Alex begins to rearrange the silverware and the napkins, first his and then Bill's. Now Bill becomes uneasy. He shifts around in his chair and folds his arms in front of him. Nevertheless, the two men keep on with their conversation. Finally, Alex slides the breadbasket along the edge of the table until it is very close to Bill. At this point, Bill becomes very irritated, even though his chat with Alex has been very pleasant. Bill is puzzled by the way he feels, and Alex cannot understand his friend's irritation. How can their behavior be explained?

Anyone listening to Alex and Bill's friendly conversation would suppose that everything was fine. The explanation cannot be found in what Bill or Alex said, but rather, in what they did. Their actions represent a concept that is crucial to our total communication. Alex used his body as an instrument of language. The way his body moved in the space that surrounded them told Bill that Alex was threatening him.

Check the box next to the correct answer.

1. Alex's fiddling with items on the table shows that _____ .
  ☐ a. he likes to play with the silverware in a restaurant
  ☐ b. he is still trying to relax
  ☐ c. he is Bill's friend

2. Bill does not become uneasy about what Alex is doing until
   _____ .
  ☐ a. Alex knocks the breadbasket off the table
  ☐ b. Alex shifts around in his chair
  ☐ c. Alex moves Bill's silverware and napkin

3. Bill becomes irritated because _____ .
  ☐ a. of the way Alex is moving around
  ☐ b. of something Alex said
  ☐ c. Alex has not been very pleasant

4. You could understand why Bill was irritated if _____ .
  ☐ a. you listened to the conversation
  ☐ b. you understood Alex's body movement
  ☐ c. you heard Alex threaten Bill

B.   All of us, like Alex and Bill in the story, use space to communicate. As soon as we are born, we begin to relate to the space around us. We claim a bubble of space as our own—almost as if we were staking out territory and defending it, as many animals do. We feel threatened if anyone enters it. In the story, neither Alex nor Bill owned the table in the restaurant, and yet, because it fell into the area of space each had designated as his own, each unconsciously claimed part of it as soon as he sat down. They divided the table into two equal parts; an invisible line formed a barrier between Alex's space and Bill's. When Alex started to move things over onto Bill's "side" of the table, Bill became uneasy. He felt threatened by Alex who, because of his movements, was subconsciously identified as an intruder into Bill's area of space. Even though Bill knew Alex was his friend and he knew that Alex meant no real harm, he was antagonized by Alex's actions.

Each day we encounter situations in which our handling of space plays an important role. Dr. Edward T. Hall, an anthropolgoist, has developed a science called "proxemics" that describes how people utilize space and how their use of space communicates certain facts and signals to other people. Dr. Hall contends that there are four different "zones" of space that a person marks out for himself. His "public zone" of space is the one which strangers may enter without his feeling threatened. His "social zone" is the zone where strangers and acquaintances may enter to conduct formal or informal business. His "personal zone" of space is one in which only friends and relatives are welcomed. Finally, a person has an "intimate zone" where only the persons that are the very closest to him are allowed—persons such as husband or wife, mother or father. We feel uncomfortable in a crowded room when others come too close to our "personal zone" of space. If we bump into someone on a bus, in the street, or anywhere, we excuse ourselves, not so much because we think that we have hurt them, but because we realize that we have invaded their "personal" space.

Check the box next to the correct answer.

1. As soon as we are born _____ .
- ☐ a. we begin to feel threatened
- ☐ b. we begin to use space around us to communicate
- ☐ c. we begin to use bubbles to communicate

2. Like animals, Alex and Bill were unconsciously _____ .
- ☐ a. staking out territory on the table
- ☐ b. trying to own the restaurant
- ☐ c. claiming to own the table

3. Proxemics is a science that describes _____ .
☐ a. how people threaten each other
☐ b. how people utilize space
☐ c. how people communicate with strangers

4. Crowded places often make us feel uneasy because we _____ .
☐ a. feel that our "personal" and even our "intimate" space is being threatened
☐ b. have to keep excusing ourselves for invading other people's "personal" or "intimate" space when we bump into them
☐ c. both a. and b.

C.   What is communicated through the use of space can also vary from one culture to another. Peoples of different cultures have different concepts of what their zones of space should be. For example, people of Western countries often complain that the Arab is guilty of being impolite because he likes to be very close to the person with whom he is speaking. This close speaking distance is, of course, natural and correct for the Arab peoples. They have defined their "social," "personal," and "intimate" zones differently from those of the Western nations. For this reason, people such as the British, Germans, or Americans find themselves uncomfortable with this behavior of the Arab. In their countries, a larger distance between speakers is required.

In Japan, where a dense population makes crowded conditions a way of life, it would seem logical to conclude that the Japanese people exhibit no concept of "personal" or "intimate" space. Actually the contrary is true. The Japanese have a very definite idea of space. To them, a person's house is an area of "personal" space, and thus they resent intrusion into their homes. They see the shape and arrangement of space as having tangible meaning. This is evident in their flower arrangements and art, where units of space blend together to form an integrated whole. Westerners, on the other hand, see space as the distance between two objects. To them space is empty.

From all these situations, we can conclude one important thing—people can benefit from understanding how they use space to communicate.

Check the box next to the correct answer.

1. What is communicated through the use of space is _____ .
☐ a. the same for all people
☐ b. different for all people
☐ c. different for different cultures

2. Arabs sometimes make Westerners feel uncomfortable because
_____ .

- [ ] a. speakers stand close together in Arab cultures
- [ ] b. a larger distance between speakers is required in Arab cultures
- [ ] c. they aren't polite

3. For the Japanese, space _____ .
- [ ] a. is the distance between two objects
- [ ] b. has tangible meaning
- [ ] c. is not important

4. The important thing that we can conclude from this article is that
_____ .

- [ ] a. Westerners should learn to do flower arrangements and art where units of space blend together
- [ ] b. people must learn how to stand closer together when they are speaking
- [ ] c. people must learn to understand how they use space to communicate

Composition

Write a composition of four or five paragraphs on the topic of your country—where you were born, or the country in which you are living now. Follow the outline below.

Introduction: Introduce the reader to your country by giving general information about location, size, and population.

Discussion: Write two or three paragraphs, each about a different aspect of your country. The following aspects could be discussed:
- the history of your country (when it was discovered, gained its independence, etc.)
- the geographical features
- the economy (what it grows, exports, imports, etc.)
- the people (their origins, religion, and other characteristics)

Conclusion: Write a paragraph summarizing your feelings about your country, based on what you have said about it in the discussion section of the composition.

Word Game

Below are some lists of related words or themes. Cross out the word that does not belong to the category, and then think of a title for the list.

animals		
cat	bus	artist
horse	subway	doctor
~~needle~~	plane	engineer
cow	airport	teacher
skunk	car	lawyer
ostrich	bike	medicine

red	yell	play
mauve	scream	narrative
yellow	whisper	essay
tan	shout	poem
blue	bellow	concert
fish	holler	short story
brown	screech	novel